LEARN CHINESE

Traditional & Simplified

LANGUAGE WORKBOOK FOR BEGINNERS

POLYSCHOLAR

www.polyscholar.com

POLYSCHOLAR

www.polyscholar.com

CONTENTS

Tip: This book works best with gel pens, pencils, biros and similar media. Take care with markers and ink, as heavy or wet media may result in paper bleed or transfer through to the pages below. Here are some

HOW TO USE THIS BOOK

As with learning any language, repetition is one of the fastest ways to soak it up. This workbook contains carefully designed instruction pages that will teach you how to write each character, with space to practice your new-found Chinese calligraphy knowledge:

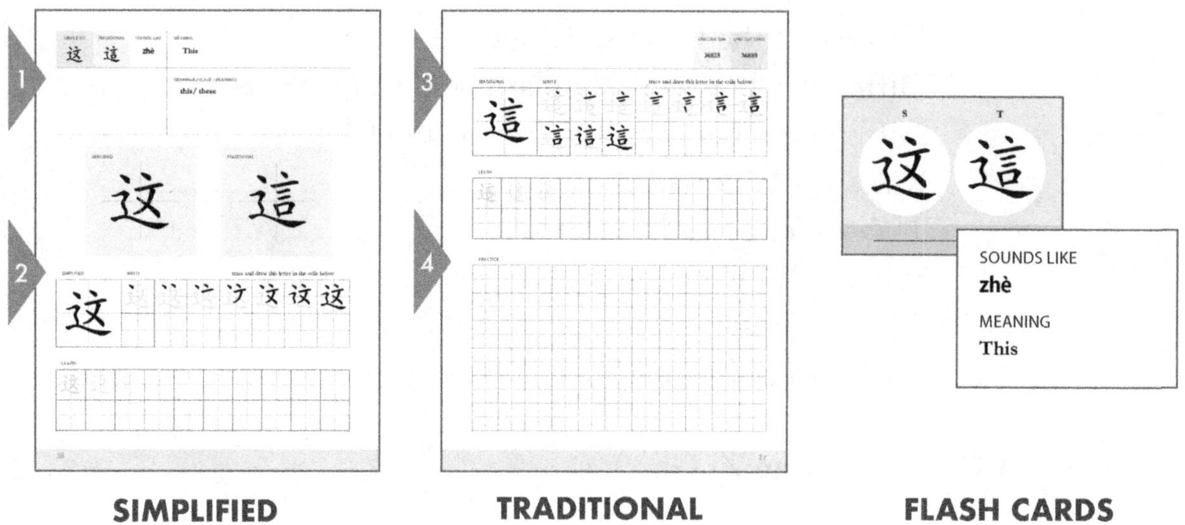

SIMPLIFIED **TRADITIONAL** **FLASH CARDS**

Towards the back of this workbook you will find additional grids that you can use after you learn how to write some (or even all) of the Simplified and Traditional Chinese characters - these grid pages are referred to as Pinyin Tian Zi Ge or 拼音田字格 in Simplified and Traditional Chinese.

The final part of this workbook contains a set of flash card style pages that can either be photocopied or cut out. They are a great way to help you memorize the symbols and test your knowledge. Younger learners should seek help from an adult to cut them out!

HISTORY OF THE CHINESE LANGUAGE

Chinese is one of the most widely spoken language in the world, with at least 1.5 billion speakers. China is the only country that boasts an uninterrupted cultural heritage due to the strong inclusiveness and assimilation of its national culture, making Chinese characters one of the few uninterrupted written forms in the world.

Chinese is an analytical language, typically with 2 to 13 tones. The Chinese character system is a kind of ideographic character, which has both ideographic and phonological functions. Chinese includes two parts: spoken and written. Ancient written Chinese is known as classical Chinese, while modern written Chinese is known as vernacular Chinese, which is standardized by modern standard Chinese.

The history of Chinese can be divided into three stages. The first stage is the picture and text stage. The writing before the Shang Dynasty (c.1600-1046 B.C) belongs to this stage. There has been a saying in China since ancient times that Chinese characters and painting share the same origin because the earliest source of Chinese writing was painting. The origin of Chinese characters is primitive pictures; the "pictorial" form used by primitive people has transformed from a primitive picture into an ideographic symbol.

The second stage is based on ideographic characters, with ideographic characters as the main body. From the inscriptions on bones and tortoise shells to the characters of the Qin Dynasty (221-207 B.C.) all belong to this stage. The oracles that appeared in the Shang dynasty around the 14th century B.C. are widely considered to be the first form of Chinese characters. They have been developed to this day, with a history of 3,000 to 4,000 years.

The third stage is mainly composed of pictophonetic characters, with some pictophonetic characters and phonographic characters retained. This stage continues from the Qin and Han (202 B.C.-220) dynasties to the present. In the process, various types of fonts such as variety art, block, floating cloud, and variants were born.

DIFFERENCE BETWEEN MANDARIN AND CHINESE

Spoken Chinese can be divided into standard languages and dialects. Chinese dialects are popular in certain area. There are ten major Chinese dialects in China, including Mandarin, Cantonese, Min Chinese and so on. Common Chinese, also known as Yayan (elegant language), has been used since the Spring and Autumn Period and the Warring States Period (770 B.C.-221 B.C.). Modern common Chinese is also known as Mandarin. Mandarin is one of the Chinese dialects, and it is used as the official standard or common language currently stipulated by the Chinese government.

Mandarin uses the Beijing pronunciation as the basic pronunciation, the northern dialect as the basic dialect, and the typical modern vernacular writings as the grammatical norms. Mandarin is also used in official occasions in Taiwan, but the accent is slightly different from Mandarin in the mainland.

Mandarin combines ancient Chinese and northern minority languages.

In summary, mandarin is a dialect used as the common language in Chinese.

DIFFERENCES BETWEEN CANTONESE AND CHINESE

Cantonese is a Chinese dialect popular in Southern China. It is quite different from other dialects in China. The initial consonants, finals, and tones of Cantonese still retain some of the characteristics of medieval Chinese sounds. In terms of initial consonants, the lingual sound of Mandarin is pronounced in Cantonese with a root tongue sound. In terms of vowels, Cantonese retains some rhyme endings of Middle Ancient Chinese sounds. In terms of tone, Mandarin has only four tones, while Cantonese has as many as nine tones.

DIFFERENCES IN VOCABULARY

Cantonese is more different from Mandarin in the following aspects:

a) Cantonese retains many elements of ancient Chinese, using mostly monosyllabic words, while Mandarin is mostly bisyllabic words. For example 尾巴 (Mandarin) and 尾 (Cantonese), 眼睛 (Mandarin) and 眼 (Cantonese).

b) For disyllabic words, the word order of Cantonese is opposite to that of Mandarin. The central word in Cantonese comes first, and the modifier comes after. E.g.,公鸡 (Mandarin) and 鸡公 (Cantonese); 客人 (Mandarin) and 人客 (Cantonese); 喜欢(Mandarin) and E.g., 公鸡 Cantonese).

c) Words about auspiciousness and wishfulness are preferred in Cantonese, and thus indecent, unlucky, or taboo words are used less frequently. For example, 苦瓜 (Mandarin) and 凉瓜 (Cantonese)；鸡脚 (Mandarin)and 凤爪 (Cantonese). Numbers in Cantonese emphasize auspicious meanings, such as 2 in Mandarin is read as 易(easy), and 8 in Mandarin is read as 发 (rich).

d) Cantonese preserve many ancient words and special dialect words. E.g., 谢谢 (Mandarin) and 唔该 (Cantonese), 漂亮 (Mandarin) and 靓 (Cantonese)；不好 (Mandarin) and 弊 (Cantonese).

e) Preserve some nostalgic life expressions in Cantonese. For example, drinking tea: 喝茶 (Mandarin) and 饮茶 (Cantonese); Payroll: 发工资 (Mandarin) and 出粮, Money钱 (Mandarin) and 银纸 (Cantonese).

DIFFERENCES IN GRAMMAR

Grammatically, there are also differences between Cantonese and Mandarin, where adverbial modifiers are often placed after verbs. For example, if you look first - if you look first: if I go first - if I go first; I'm more than you - I'm more than you, wait. Also, the word order of double objects is often reversed, such as: Give you a pen - give you a pen.

DIFFERENCES IN TONE

In terms of tone, Cantonese fully retains the tonal pattern of the middle ancient Chinese language, which is divided into yin and yang for the four tones. It is the most complete language for retaining the tone of the ancient Chinese language and plays an important role in reciting and studying literary works such as ancient Chinese poetry. Cantonese contains six rhyme endings: p, t, k, n, m, and ng. It does not have the features of northern dialects such as curling, rhyming, and neutral tones.

RULES FOR WRITING CHINESE

China is a country with a vast territory and complex dialects. In ancient times, it was impossible to achieve language standardization, but Chinese characters were a popular tool for written language communication throughout the country. It means that the content in different dialects can be same in written Chinese.

There are two orders of writing Chinese. One is written vertically from top to bottom of each column, and columns on the right will be written first. The other is to write horizontally in a line from left to right, and rows will be from top to bottom. The first one is a traditional one, which was suitable for writing with soft pens. The second one is suitable for the current hard pen. Currently, the mainstream way of writing Chinese is from left to right row by row. In some areas, such as Taiwan, writing Chinese from top to bottom from right to left also exists. In the mainland of China, some books still follow the traditional writing style.

Chinese characters are of rationality. Character is a symbolic system that can be divided into rational and irrational characters. The so-called irrationality refers to pure phonetic characters, such as borrowed characters, syllabic characters, and alphabetic characters, which are purely symbols and have no direct connection with the things to be expressed. The so-called rational characters like Chinese characters, in addition to indicating the pronunciation of words, are also symbols representing the shape and class of things. For example, Chinese word 水 (water) evolved from the shape of the hieroglyph water. It has two functions, that is form and pronunciation. In Chinese word洋(ocean), the left part indicates the category of water, and the right part indicates the pronunciation. It is called pictophonetic character, the main body of Chinese characters that facilitates recognition and memory.

THE ORDER OF CHINESE STOKES

There are eight basic strokes of traditional Chinese characters. There are variations for each basic stroke. All these strokes can be classified into eight basic types: dot, horizontal, vertical, left falling, right falling, rising stroke, vertical turning and vertical hook.

Eight basic strokes in Chinese characters

Stroke	Name	Example
丶	点 (diǎn) dot	杰、洲
一	横 (héng) horizontal	一、二
丨	竖 (shù) vertical	十、利
丿	撇 (piě) left falling	八、人
㇏	捺 (nà) right falling	个、义
㇀	提 (tí) rising stroke	刁、习
ㄥ	竖折 (shù zhé) vertical turning	山、匹
亅	竖钩 (shù gōu) vertical hook	利、提

Most Chinese characters are formed by a combination of two or three of the stokes above. Different characters can be created with the same stokes, stoke orders or even combinations.

RULES FOR WRITING CHINESE

There are some generally accepted rules in writing Chinese.

General rules of stroke order in Chinese include the following:

a) Left falling before right falling, e.g., 人 (people)and 八 (eight)

b) First horizontal and then vertical, e.g., 十 (ten), 干 (do), 玉 and (jade)

c) From top to bottom, e.g., 二 (two), 三 (three) and 音 (sound).

d) From left to right, e.g., 他 (he), 她 (she)and 湖 (lake)

e) First outside, then inside, e.g., 问 (ask) and 同 (agree)

f) From outside to inside and then close, e.g., 国 (country), 园 (garden), and 圆 (circle)

g) First in the middle and then on both sides, e.g., 小 (small, 水 (water), and 永 (forever)

h) Other rules

1) Dot(s) on the top or left of an character should be written first. E.g., 海 (sea) and 衣(cloth).

2) Dot(s) on the top right of or in the character should be written at last. E.g., 我 (I), 犬 (dog), and 凡 (ordinary or every).

3) Characters with surrounding structures on the right top or left top should be written from outside to inside. E.g., 厅 (hall)and 屋 (house).

4) Characters with surrounding structures on the lower left should be written from inside to outside. E.g., 远 (farway)and 建 (build).

5) Characters with surrounding structures on the left, bottom and right , should be written from inside to outside. E.g., 凶 (fierce) and 山 (mountain).

6) Characters with surrounding structures on the top, left and right should be written from outside to inside. E.g., 同 (same)and 风 (wind).

7) Characters with surrounding structures on the top, bottom and left should be written in the following order: the top, the inside and the bottom. E.g., 医 (doctor), 巨 (giant), and 区 (district).

SPELLING (PINYIN)

Chinese pronunciation is characterized by simple syllable structures, distinct syllable boundaries, and tone. The syllable structure of Chinese has a strong regularity.

INITIAL CONSONANTS AND FINALS

Traditionally, in Chinese, a syllable is divided into three parts: initial consonant, final consonant, and tone. An initial consonant refers to a consonant at the beginning of a syllable. If there is no initial consonant at the beginning of a syllable, it is called a zero-vowel syllable. A vowel refers to the component behind the initial consonant in a syllable, which can be just a vowel, a combination of vowels, or a combination of vowels and consonants. There are 23 initial and 24 final consonants in Mandarin.

INITIAL CONSONANTS

b	p	m	f	d
t	n	l	g	k
h	j	q	x	zh
ch	sh	r	z	c
s	y	w		

FINAL CONSONANTS

Traditionally, there are 35 finals in Chinese, which are simplified into 24 for beginners currently. According to the structure, finals can be divided into simple vowels, compound vowels, nasal vowels and a special vowel.

Simple vowels	**a、o、e、i、u、ü**
Compound vowels	**ai、ei、ui、ao、ou、iu、ie、ve**
Special vowel	**er**
Nasal vowels	**an、en、in、un、vn、,ang、eng、ing、ong**

AN OVERVIEW OF PRONUNCIATION

a: The lips naturally expand, the tongue is flat, the middle of the tongue is slightly raised, and the vocal cords vibrate.

o: The lips are rounded, slightly raised, the tongue retracts, the rear of the tongue surface bulges, the tongue is centered, and the vocal cords vibrate.

e: With the mouth half open, the tongue positioned back, the corners of the mouth extended to both sides into a flat shape, and the vocal cords trembling.

i: The mouth is slightly opened into a flat shape, the tip of the tongue is pressed against the lower gingiva, the surface of the tongue is raised, close to the upper hard palate, and the vocal cords vibrate.

u: The lips are rounded and protruded into small holes, with the back of the tongue protruding and the vocal cords trembling.

ü: The lips are rounded, close together, the tip of the tongue against the lower gum, the front of the tongue is raised, and the vocal cords vibrate.

ai: First pronounce the sound of a, then slide towards i. The air flow is uninterrupted, and the pronunciation is light and short.

ei: First pronounce the sound of e, then slide towards i. The air flow is uninterrupted, and the corners of the mouth are extended to both sides.

ui: u is light and short, then slides towards ei, with the mouth shaped from round to flat.

ao: First pronounce the sound of a, then retract the tip of the tongue, lift the base of the tongue upward, close the mouth into a circle, and gently slide towards o.

ou: Start with the o sound, gradually closing the lips, raising the base of the tongue, and changing the mouth shape from large to small.

iu: Start with i, then slide towards ou, with the mouth shape from flat to round.

ie: first i, then e, the air flow is uninterrupted.

üe: First pronounce the ü sound, then slide towards e, with the mouth shape changing from round to flat.

er: pronounce e in the middle of the tongue position, then roll the tip of the tongue towards the hard palate, pronouncing both letters simultaneously

an: first pronounces the sound of a, then gradually raises the tip of the tongue to counter the upper gums and pronounce the sound of n.".

en: First pronounce the sound of e, then raise the surface of the tongue, press the tip of the tongue against the upper gums, and air flows out of the nasal cavity to pronounce the sound of n.".

in: First pronounce the sound of i, then press the tip of the tongue against the back of the lower incisor teeth, gradually reaching the hard palate, and the air flows out of the nasal cavity to pronounce the sound of n.

un: starts with a sound of u, then presses the tip of the tongue against the upper gums, and then sounds with a sound of n, allowing air to escape from the nasal cavity.

ün: First pronounce the sound of ü, then lift your tongue up against the upper gums, and the air flows out of the nasal cavity to pronounce the sound of n.

ang: First pronounce the sound of a, then press the base of the tongue against the upper soft palate, allowing air to escape from the nasal cavity, and then pronounce the sound of ng at the end of the nasal sound.
eng sounds e first, then the tip of the tongue presses against the lower gums, the base of the tongue retracts back against the soft palate, and sounds ng, allowing air to escape from the nasal cavity.

ung: The tip of the tongue touches the lower gingiva, the surface of the tongue rises to the hard palate, and the nasal cavity resonates into sound.

ong: First pronounce the o sound, then retract the base of the tongue against the soft palate, with the tongue protruding, the lips rounded, and the nasal cavity resonating.

TONES

Chinese is a tonal language, which has the function of distinguishing meanings. The number of tones in Chinese is much smaller than the initial and final consonants. Mandarin only has 4 tones.

First tone: high and level

Second tone: rising

Third tone: falling before rising

Fourth tone: falling

For example,

First tone: ma1 or mā

Second tone: ma2 or má

Third tone: ma3 or mǎ

Fourth tone: ma4 or mà

SPELLING RULES

In a syllable, the initial sound is the initial consonant, and the rest is the final consonant. The tone indicates the rise and fall of the syllable. For example, the initial consonant of汉 (Han)character is "h", the final consonant is "an", and the tone is a falling tone. If the initial consonants and vowels are the same, and the tone is different, the pronunciation and meaning are different. For example, " 汤 ", " 糖 " and " 躺 " have the same final consonant "ang", but have different tones, their sounds and meanings are different.

a) Use of y and w

In order to make the syllable boundary clear, the soundproof letters "y" and "w" should be used for syllables beginning with a zero initial. For example, the final consonant of "i" should be accompanied by y, such as yi (衣).

The vowel u should be accompanied by w, such as wu (乌).

b) The vowel "ü" should be accompanied by y, such as yu (迂), and yuan (远).

c) Use of iou, uei, and uen

When spelling these three vowels and initials, the vowel letters in the middle should be removed and written as iu, ui, and un. Such as niu (牛), gui (归), and lun (论).

If the initial consonant is zero, it should be written as you, wei, and wen according to the rules for using y and w. It can be seen that iou, uei, and uen are theoretical writing methods that do not appear in actual spelling. When analyzing the structure of vowels, iou, uei, and uen are used without omitting the form.

d) Use of ü

The vowel ü can be spelled with the five consonants j, q, x, n, and l. When j, q, x, and U are spelled together, ü should be omitted and written as u.

when n, l, and ü are combined, the two points on u cannot be omitted. 女 (female)should be spelled as nü instead of nu, 吕 should be spelled as lü, instead of lu.

e) Position of tone symbols

Tone symbols should be marked on the vowel rather than the initial consonant. The simple final has only one vowel, and the tone mark can only be placed on that vowel, such as bā (八)and t í (提).

A compound vowel with a tone mark on the first vowel, such as bái (白) and bēi (杯); The double vowel is followed by a compound vowel, and the tone sign is placed on the second vowel, such as jiā (home) and guó (country);

A triad compound vowel with a key mark on the middle vowel, such as jiāo (交) and guāi (乖). The tone of iu and ui is marked on the next vowel, and the tone of un is marked on the first vowel. Such as niú (牛) guī (归), and lùn (论).

Part 2

STROKE ORDER DIAGRAMS

SIMPLIFIED	TRADITIONAL	SOUNDS LIKE	MEANING
的	的	**de**	**Of**

GRAMMAR / USAGE / MEANINGS

truly / aim and of / really, clear (possessive particle)

SIMPLIFIED

的

TRADITIONAL

的

SIMPLIFIED

WRITE

trace and draw this letter in the cells below

LEARN

UNICODE SIM.	UNICODE TRAD.
30340	**30340**

TRADITIONAL

WRITE

trace and draw this letter in the cells below

的

丿 亻 𠂎 白 白 的 的

的

LEARN

的 的 的

PRACTICE

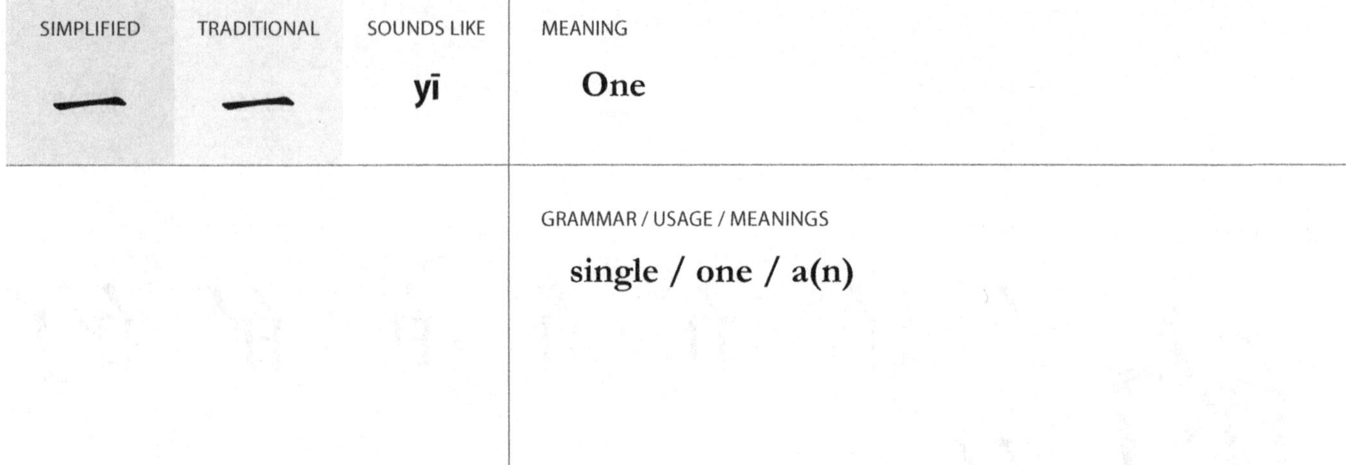

SIMPLIFIED	TRADITIONAL	SOUNDS LIKE	MEANING
一	一	**yī**	**One**

GRAMMAR / USAGE / MEANINGS

single / one / a(n)

SIMPLIFIED

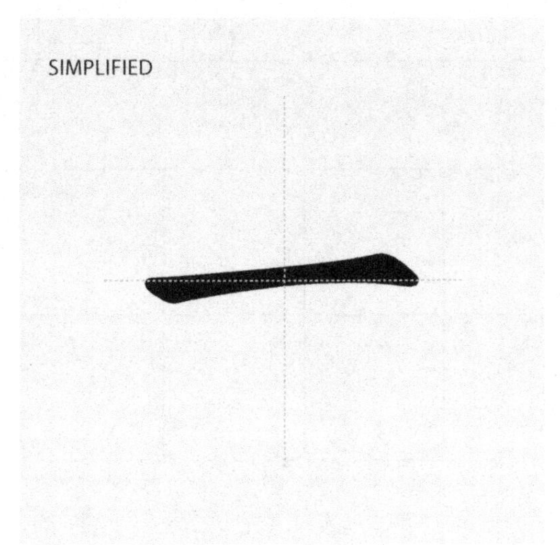

TRADITIONAL

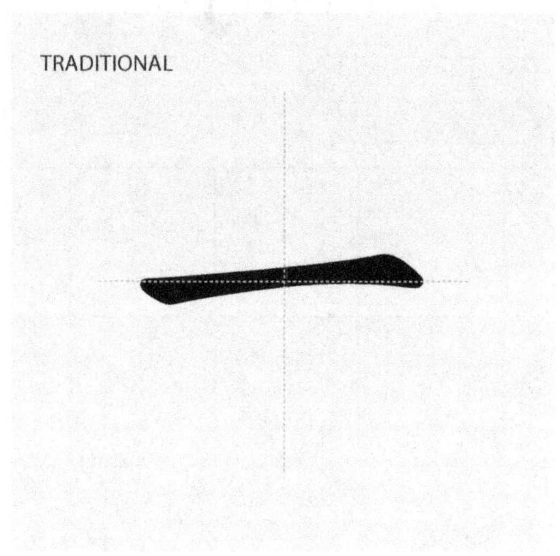

SIMPLIFIED WRITE trace and draw this letter in the cells below

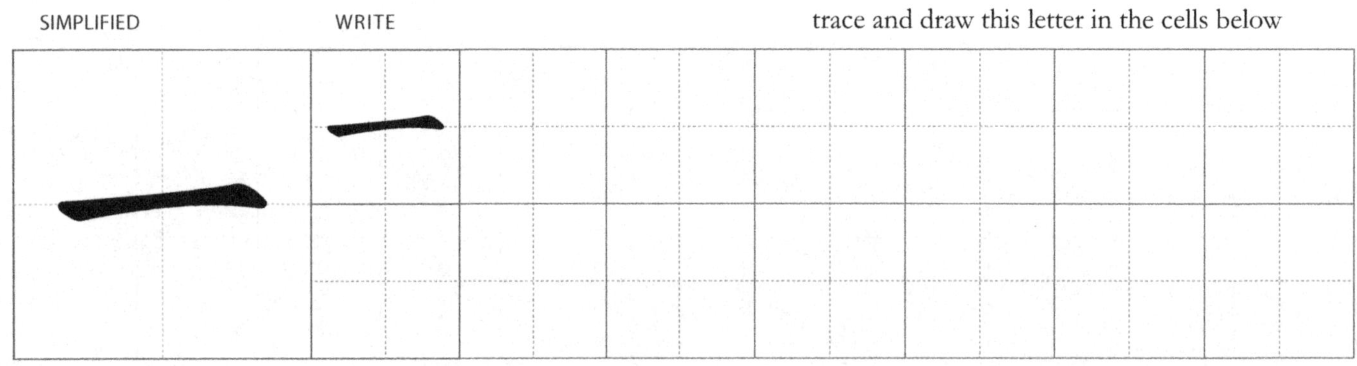

LEARN

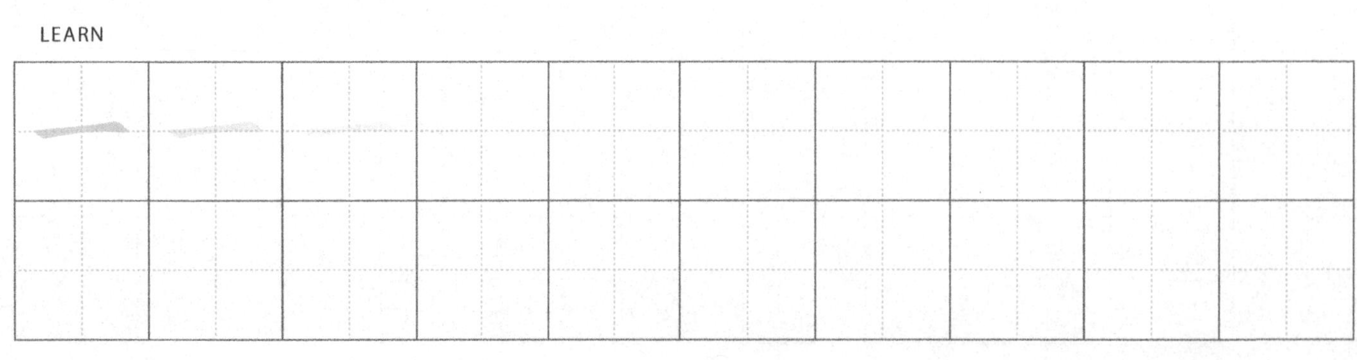

UNICODE SIM.	UNICODE TRAD.
19968	**19968**

TRADITIONAL

WRITE

trace and draw this letter in the cells below

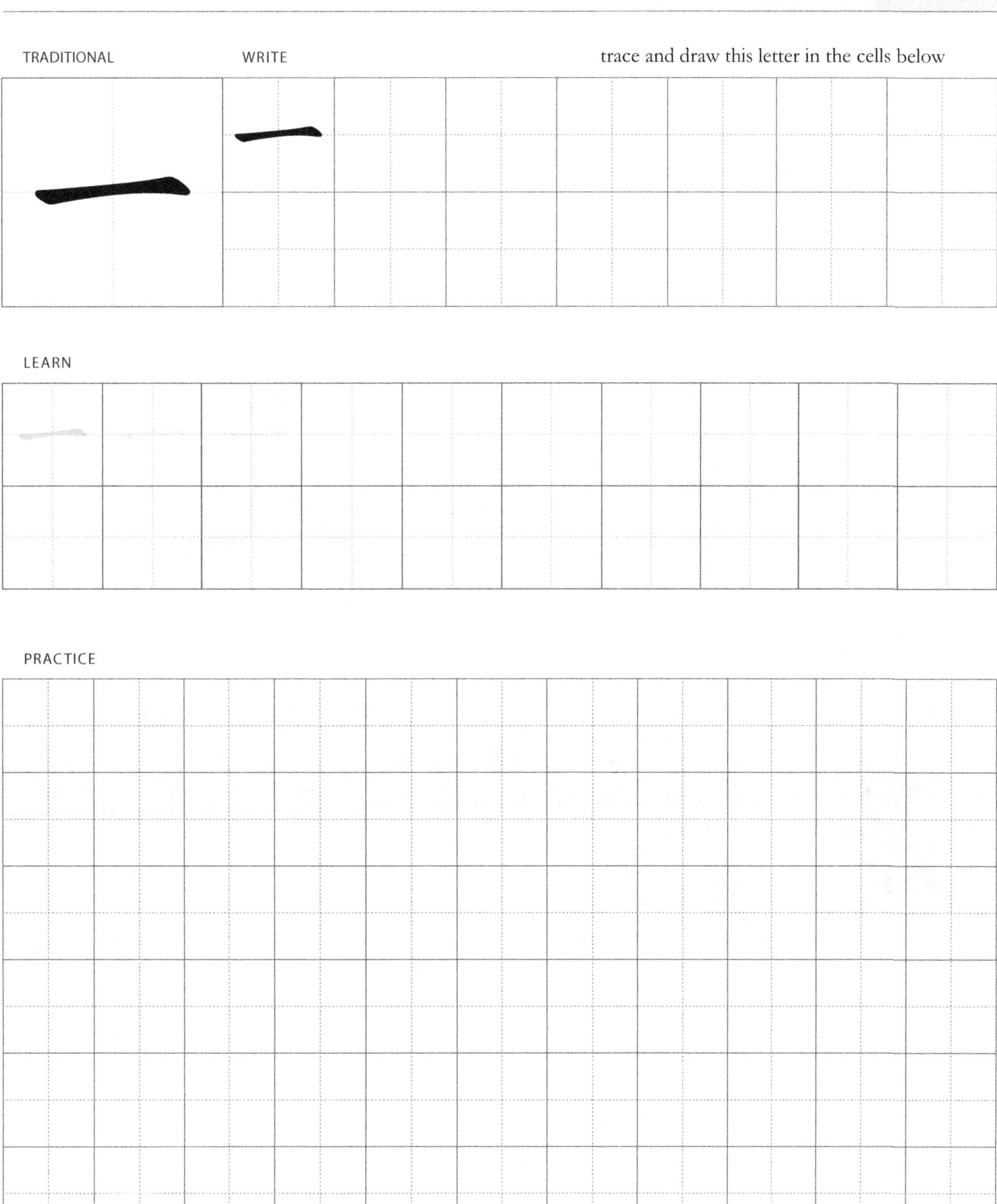

LEARN

PRACTICE

SIMPLIFIED	TRADITIONAL	SOUNDS LIKE	MEANING
是	是	shì	Yes

GRAMMAR / USAGE / MEANINGS

is, yes, are, right, am

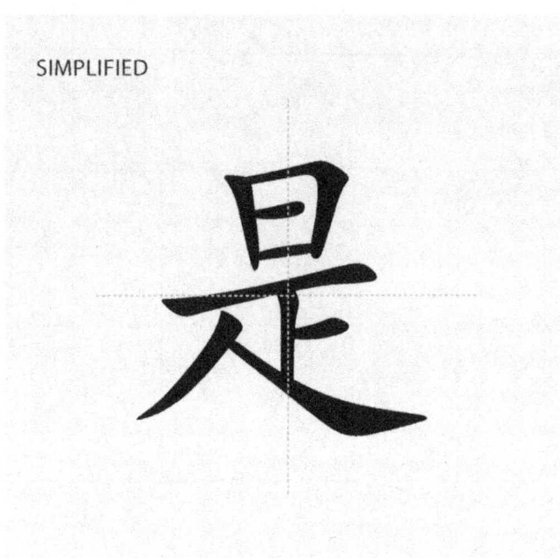

TRADITIONAL

是

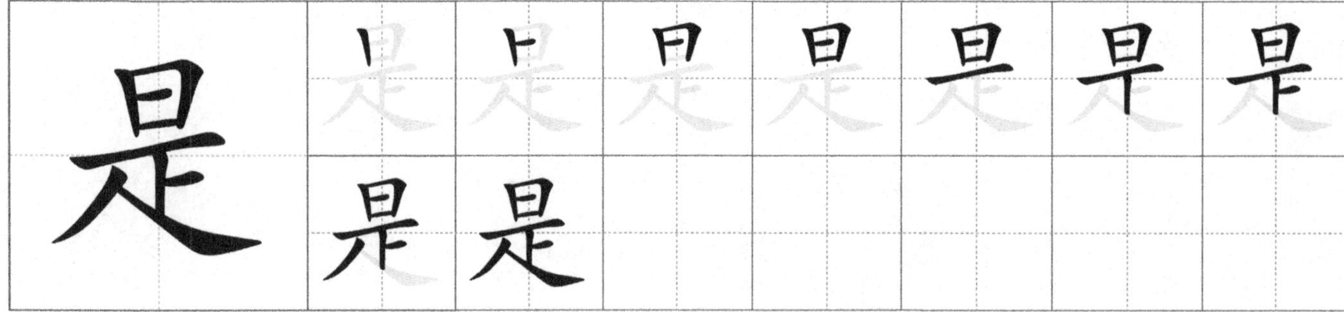

LEARN

UNICODE SIM.	UNICODE TRAD.
26159	26159

TRADITIONAL

是

WRITE

trace and draw this letter in the cells below

丨 卜 日 日 旦 早 早 昰 是

LEARN

是 是 是

PRACTICE

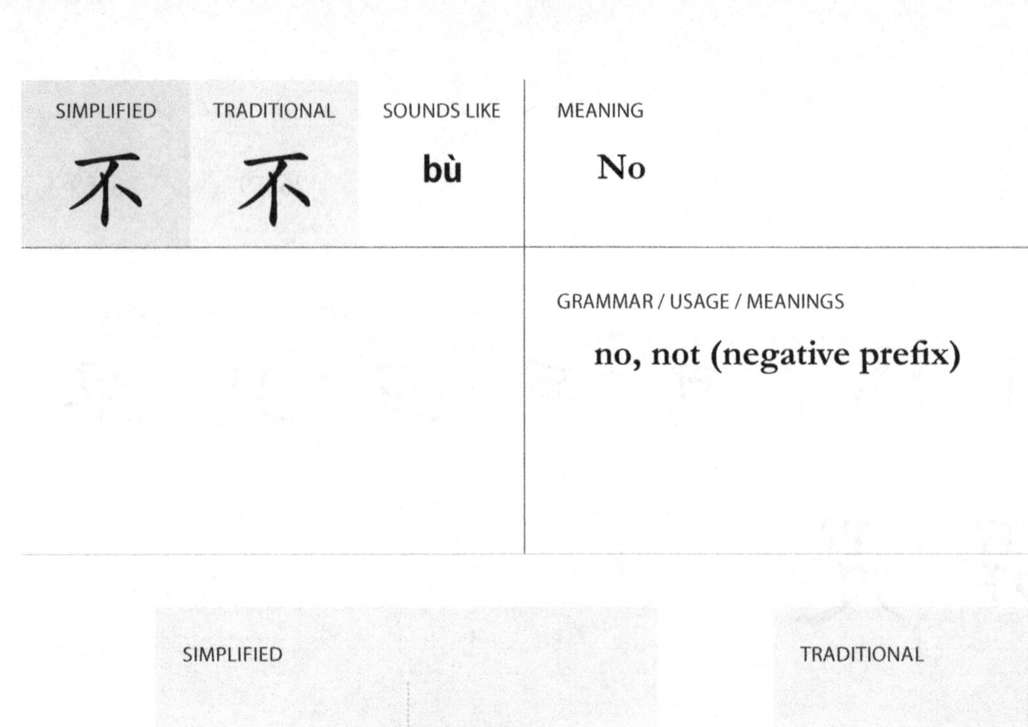

SIMPLIFIED	TRADITIONAL	SOUNDS LIKE	MEANING
不	不	**bù**	**No**

GRAMMAR / USAGE / MEANINGS

no, not (negative prefix)

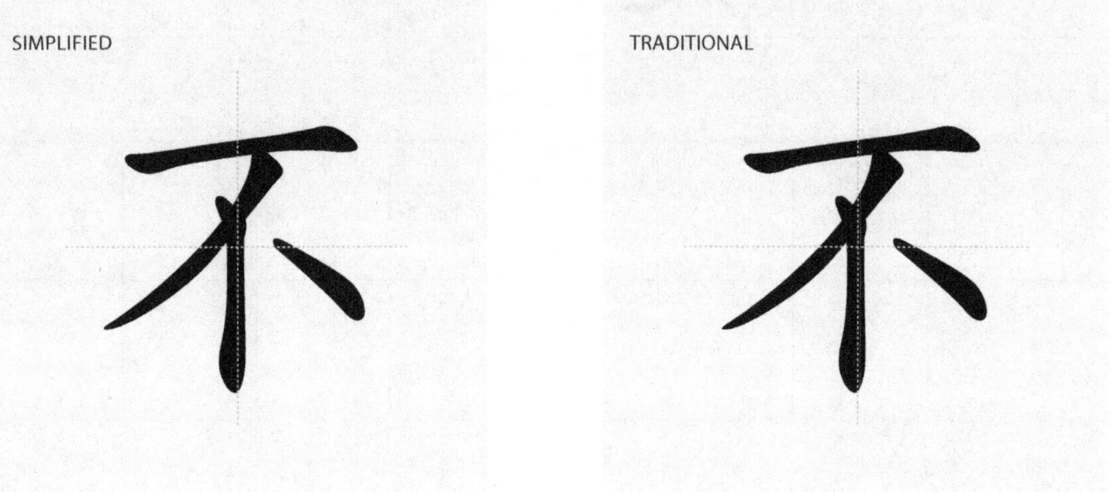

SIMPLIFIED WRITE trace and draw this letter in the cells below

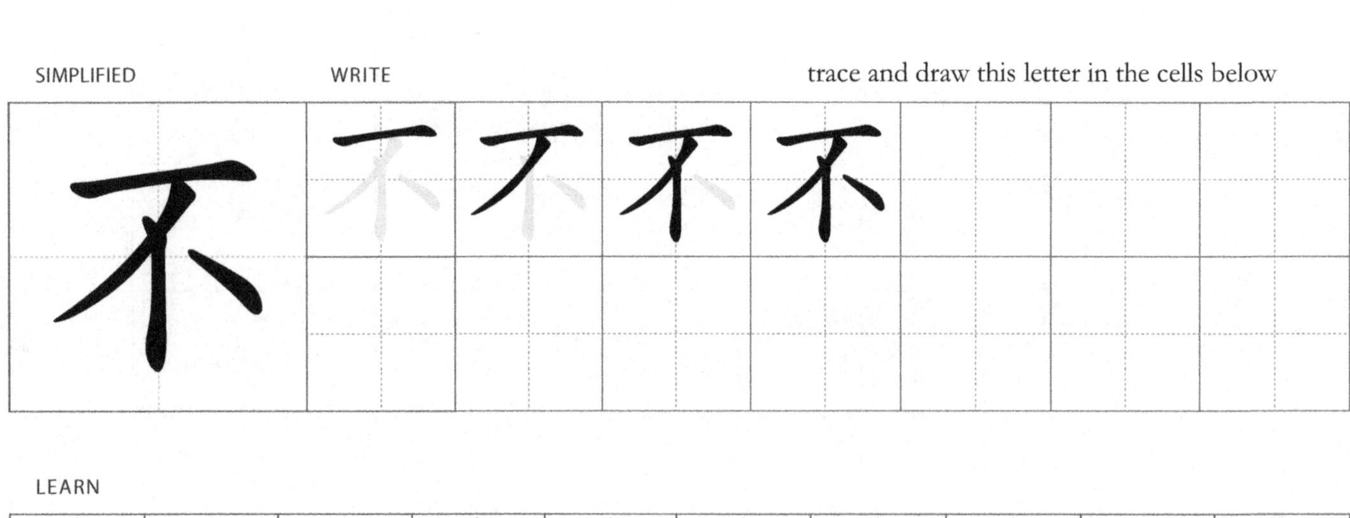

LEARN

UNICODE SIM.	UNICODE TRAD.
19981	19981

TRADITIONAL

不

WRITE

trace and draw this letter in the cells below

LEARN

PRACTICE

SIMPLIFIED	TRADITIONAL	SOUNDS LIKE	MEANING
了	了	**le/liǎo**	**Up**

GRAMMAR / USAGE / MEANINGS

to know, to understand, to know (past tense marker), (modal particle intensifying preceding clause)

SIMPLIFIED

了

TRADITIONAL

了

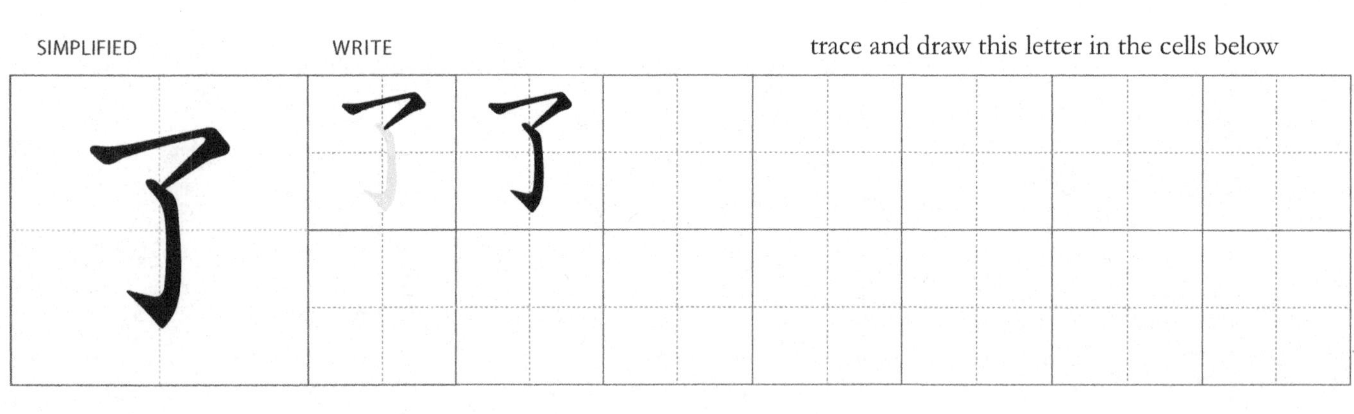

SIMPLIFIED

了

WRITE

trace and draw this letter in the cells below

LEARN

UNICODE SIM.	UNICODE TRAD.
20102	20102

TRADITIONAL

了

WRITE

trace and draw this letter in the cells below

LEARN

PRACTICE

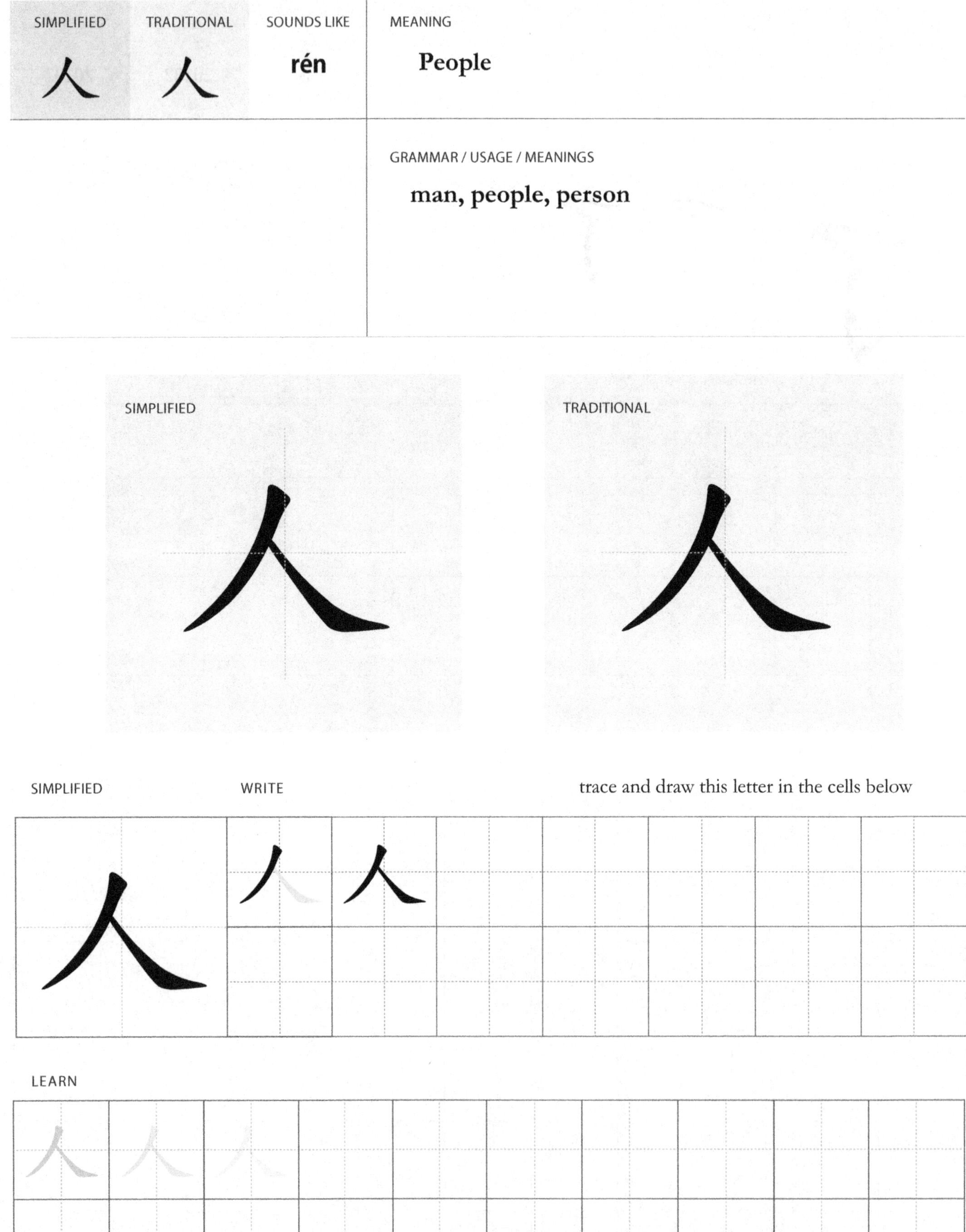
SIMPLIFIED
人
TRADITIONAL
人
SOUNDS LIKE
rén
MEANING
People
GRAMMAR / USAGE / MEANINGS
man, people, person
SIMPLIFIED
人
TRADITIONAL
人
SIMPLIFIED
WRITE
trace and draw this letter in the cells below
人
LEARN

UNICODE SIM.	UNICODE TRAD.
20154	20154

TRADITIONAL　　WRITE　　trace and draw this letter in the cells below

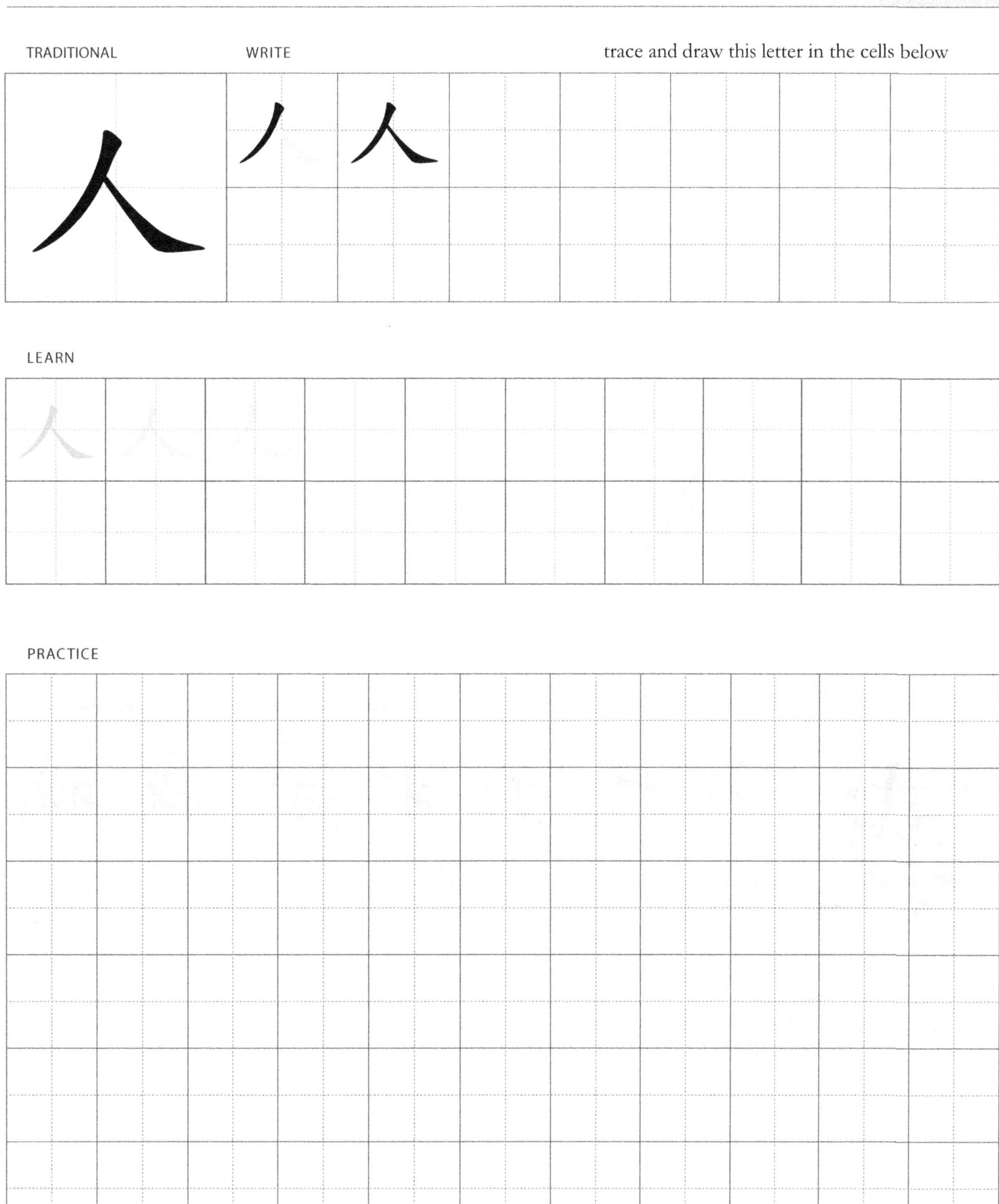

LEARN

PRACTICE

SIMPLIFIED	TRADITIONAL	SOUNDS LIKE	MEANING
我	我	wǒ	I

GRAMMAR / USAGE / MEANINGS

myself, me, I

TRADITIONAL

我

SIMPLIFIED WRITE trace and draw this letter in the cells below

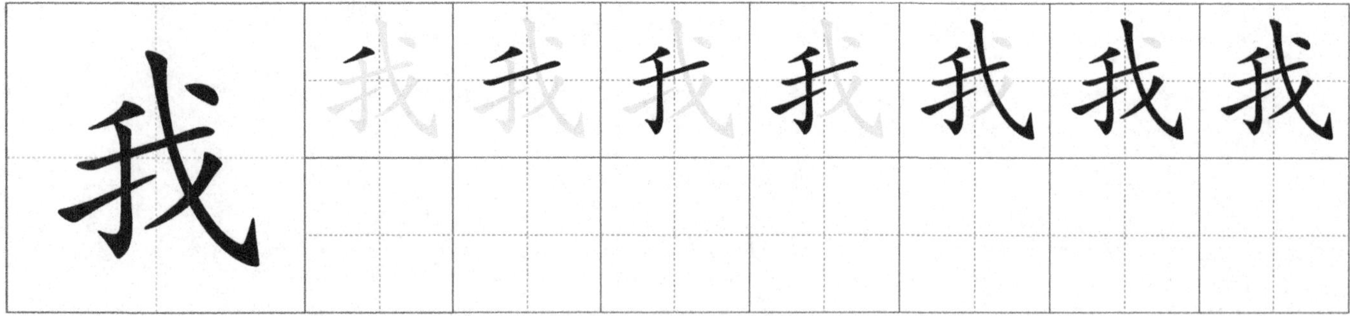

LEARN

UNICODE SIM.	UNICODE TRAD.
25105	**25105**

TRADITIONAL

我

WRITE

trace and draw this letter in the cells below

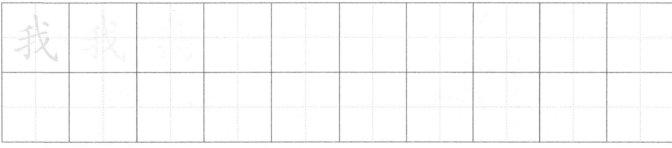

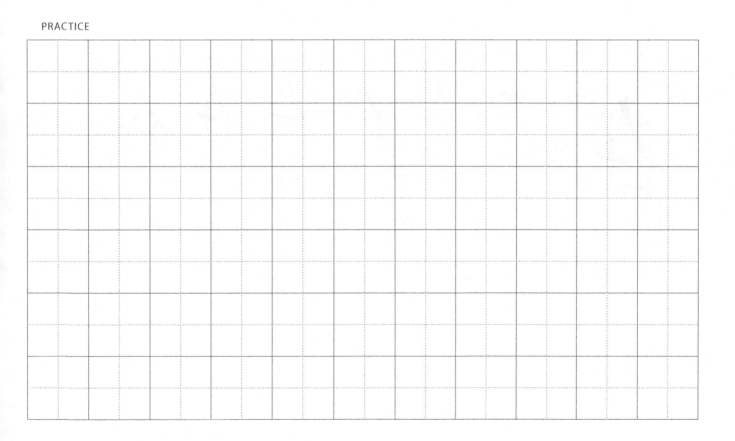

LEARN

PRACTICE

SIMPLIFIED	TRADITIONAL	SOUNDS LIKE	MEANING
在	在	zài	**In**

GRAMMAR / USAGE / MEANINGS

in, exist, (located) at

TRADITIONAL

在

trace and draw this letter in the cells below

LEARN

UNICODE SIM.	UNICODE TRAD.
22312	22312

TRADITIONAL

在

WRITE

trace and draw this letter in the cells below

LEARN

PRACTICE

SIMPLIFIED	TRADITIONAL	SOUNDS LIKE	MEANING
有	有	yǒu	There Are

GRAMMAR / USAGE / MEANINGS

to exist, to have, there is, to be, there are

SIMPLIFIED

有

WRITE

trace and draw this letter in the cells below

有 有 有 有 有 有

LEARN

有 有 有

UNICODE SIM.	UNICODE TRAD.
26377	26377

TRADITIONAL

有

WRITE

trace and draw this letter in the cells below

一 ナ 冇 有 有 有

LEARN

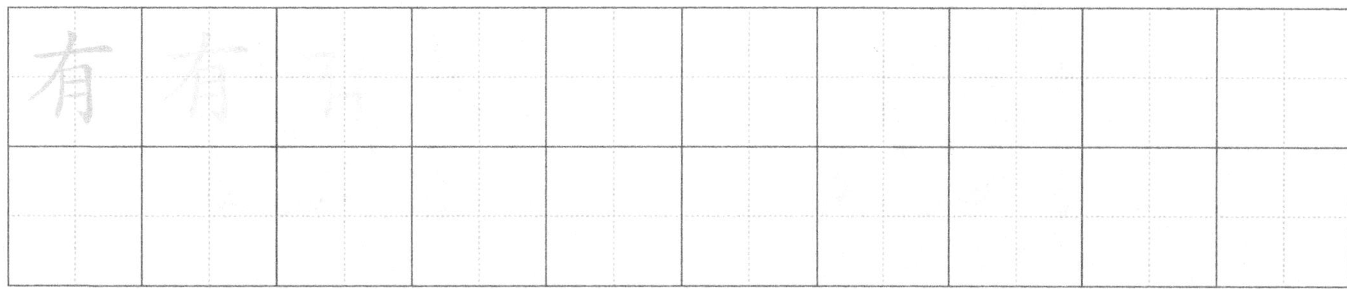

PRACTICE

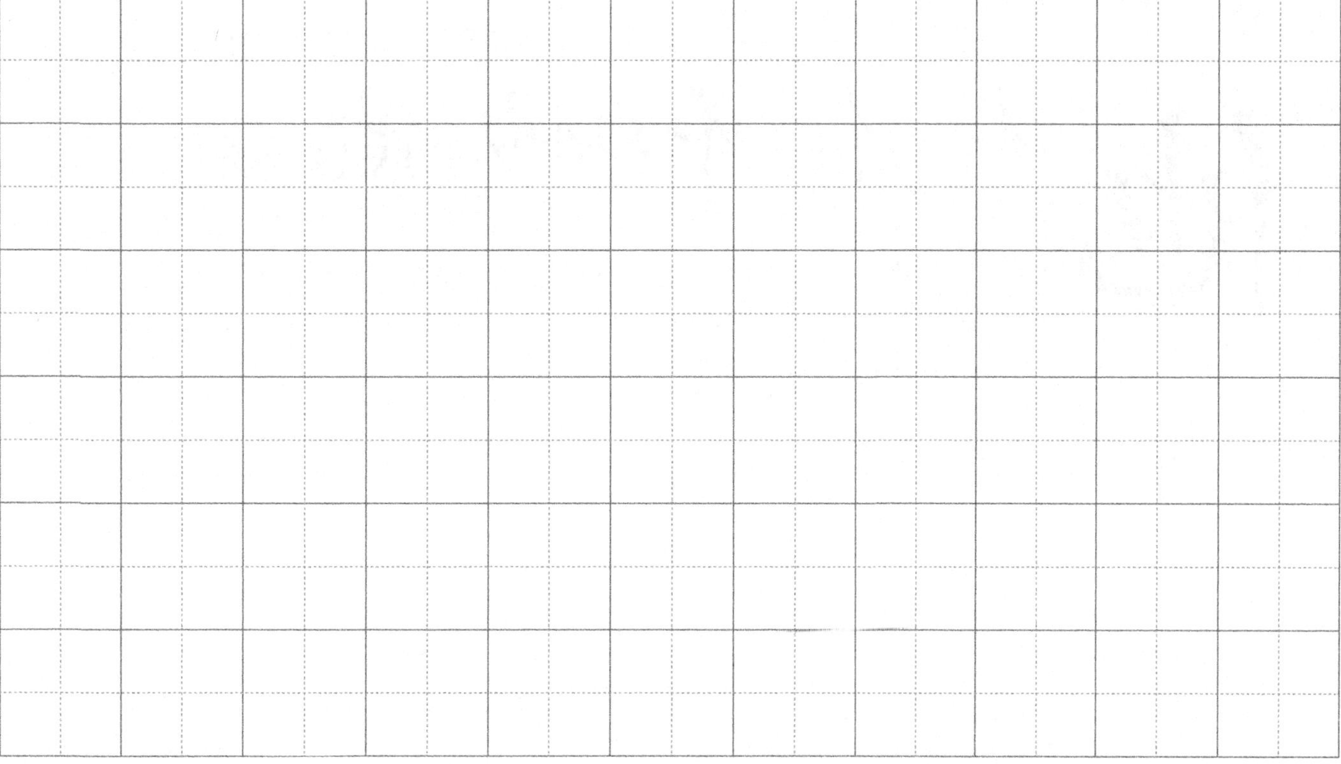

SIMPLIFIED	TRADITIONAL	SOUNDS LIKE	MEANING
他	他	tā	He

GRAMMAR / USAGE / MEANINGS

he, him

SIMPLIFIED

他

TRADITIONAL

他

SIMPLIFIED WRITE trace and draw this letter in the cells below

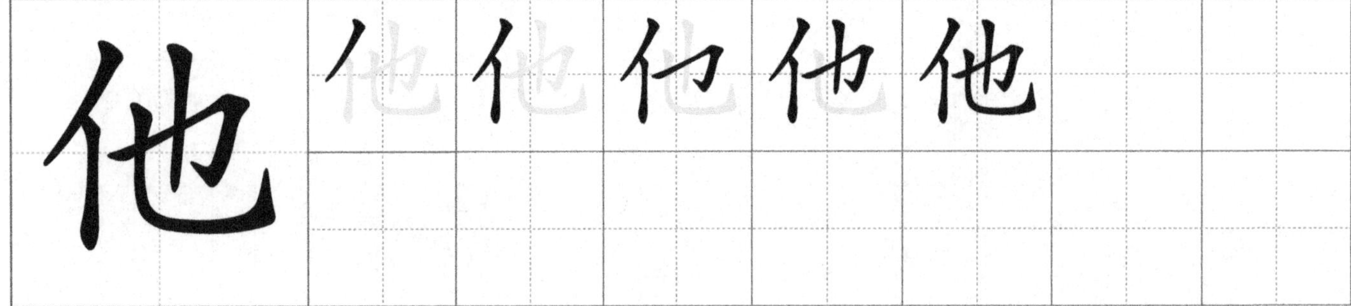

LEARN

他 他 他

UNICODE SIM.	UNICODE TRAD.
20182	20182

TRADITIONAL

他

WRITE

trace and draw this letter in the cells below

丿 亻 亻㇆ 仂 他

LEARN

他 他 他

PRACTICE

SIMPLIFIED	TRADITIONAL	SOUNDS LIKE	MEANING
这	這	**zhè**	**This**

GRAMMAR / USAGE / MEANINGS

this/ these

SIMPLIFIED WRITE trace and draw this letter in the cells below

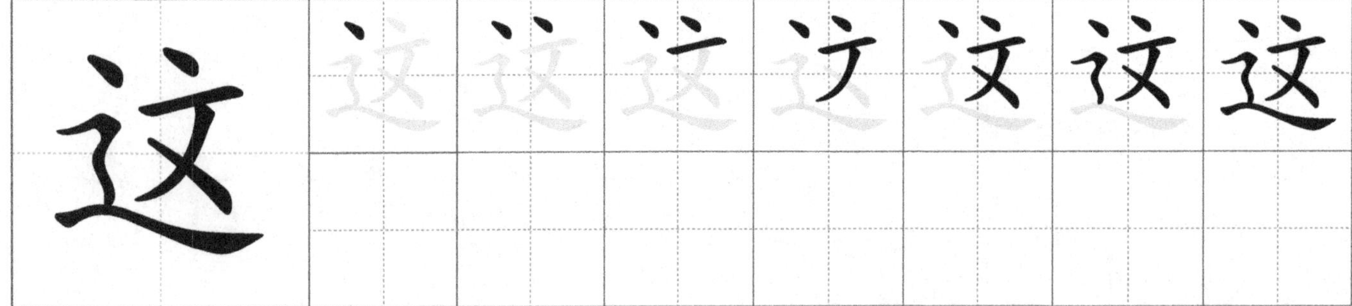

LEARN

UNICODE SIM.	UNICODE TRAD.
36825	36889

TRADITIONAL

WRITE

trace and draw this letter in the cells below

這

LEARN

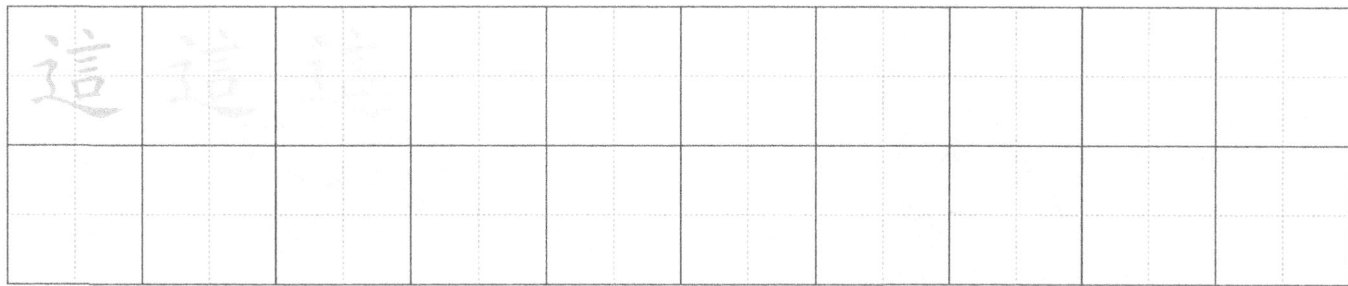

PRACTICE

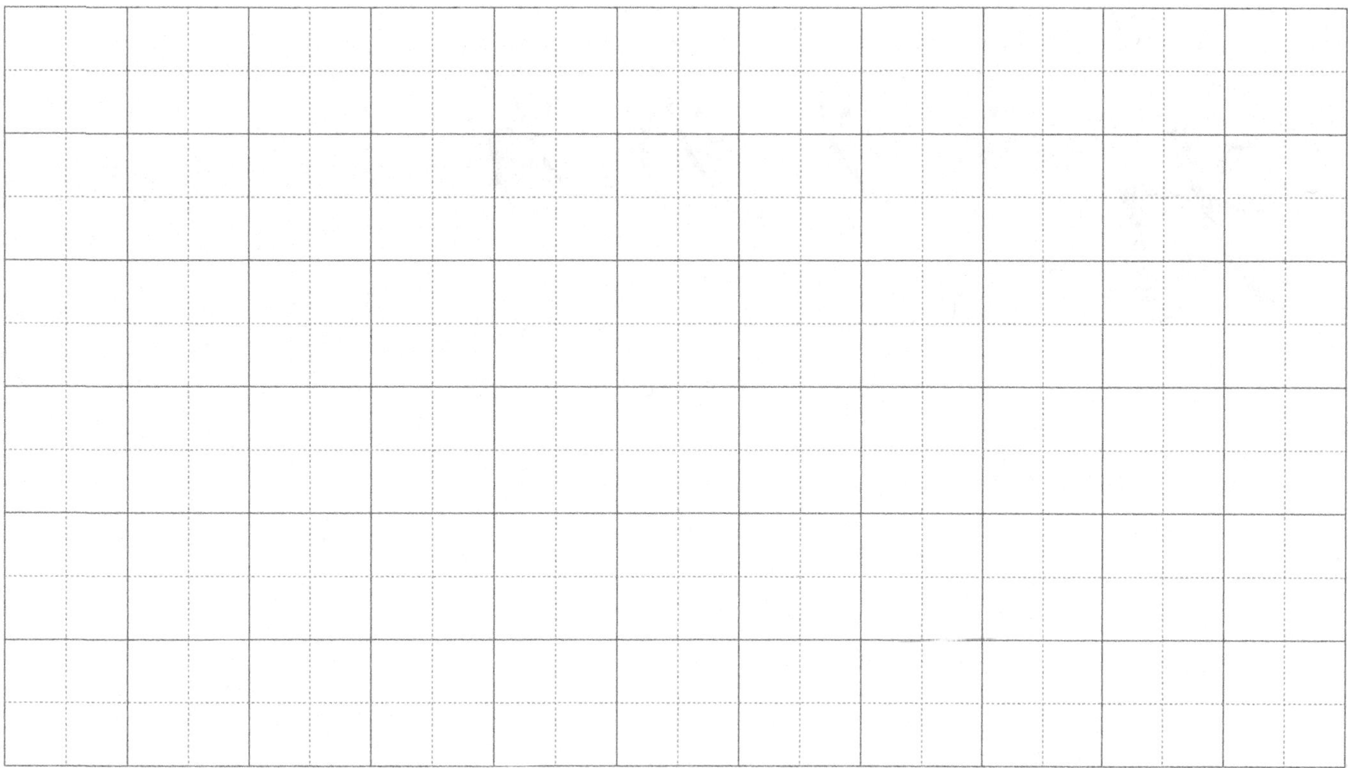

SIMPLIFIED	TRADITIONAL	SOUNDS LIKE	MEANING
为	為	**wéi / wèi**	**For**

GRAMMAR / USAGE / MEANINGS

to become / because of, for, to,act as, take..., to serve as, to do, to be, to be

SIMPLIFIED

为

TRADITIONAL

為

SIMPLIFIED

为

WRITE

trace and draw this letter in the cells below

LEARN

UNICODE SIM.	UNICODE TRAD.
20026	**28858**

TRADITIONAL

為

WRITE

trace and draw this letter in the cells below

LEARN

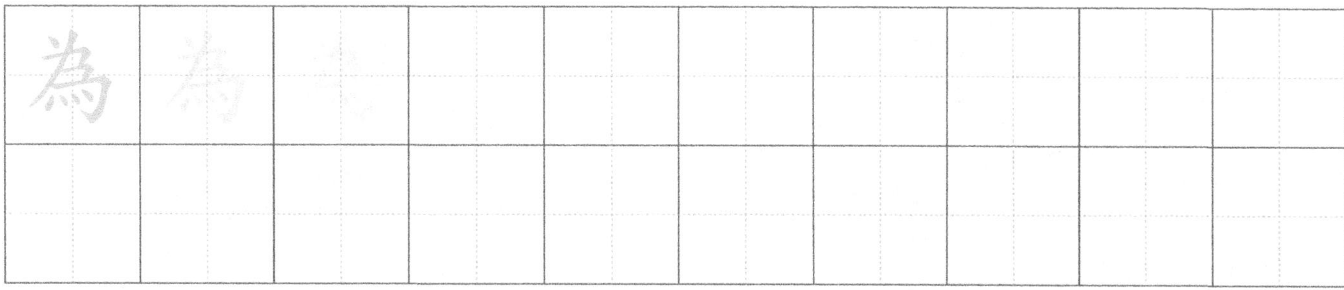

PRACTICE

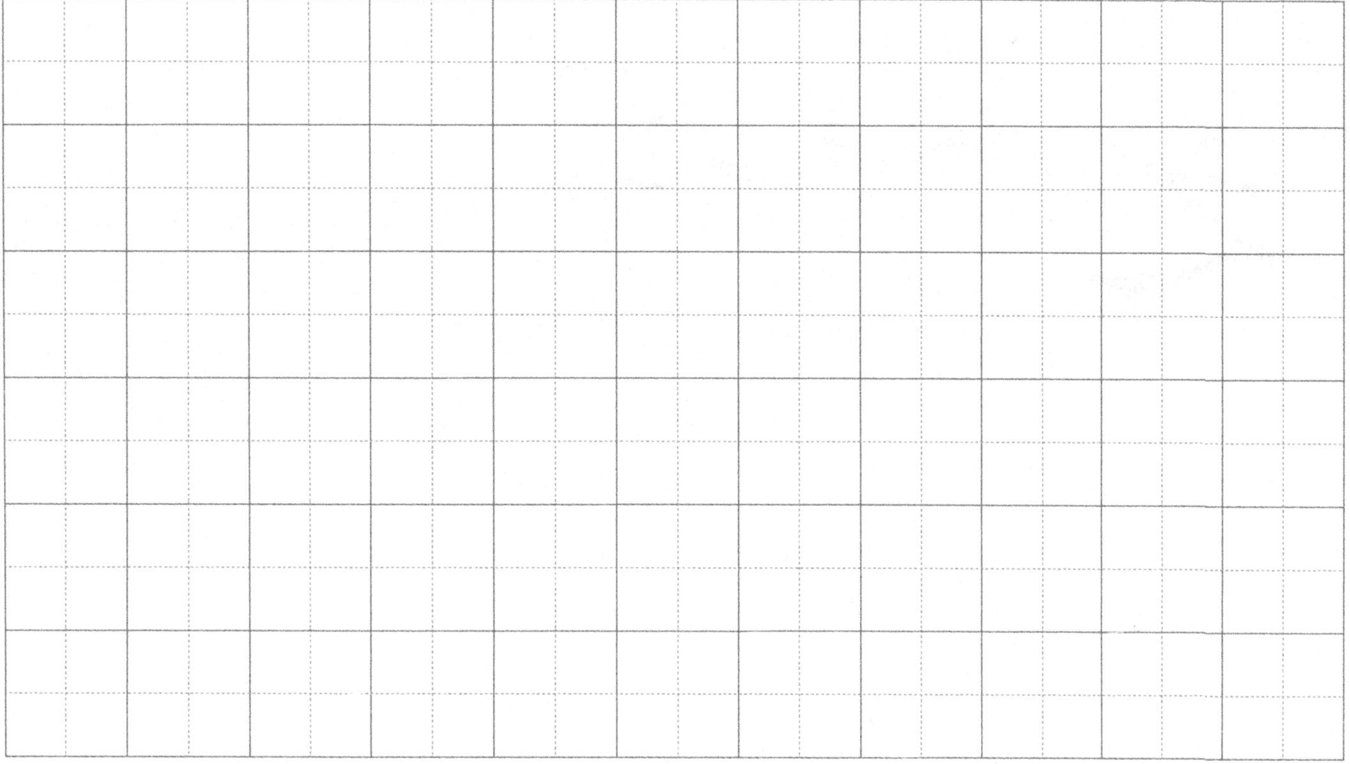

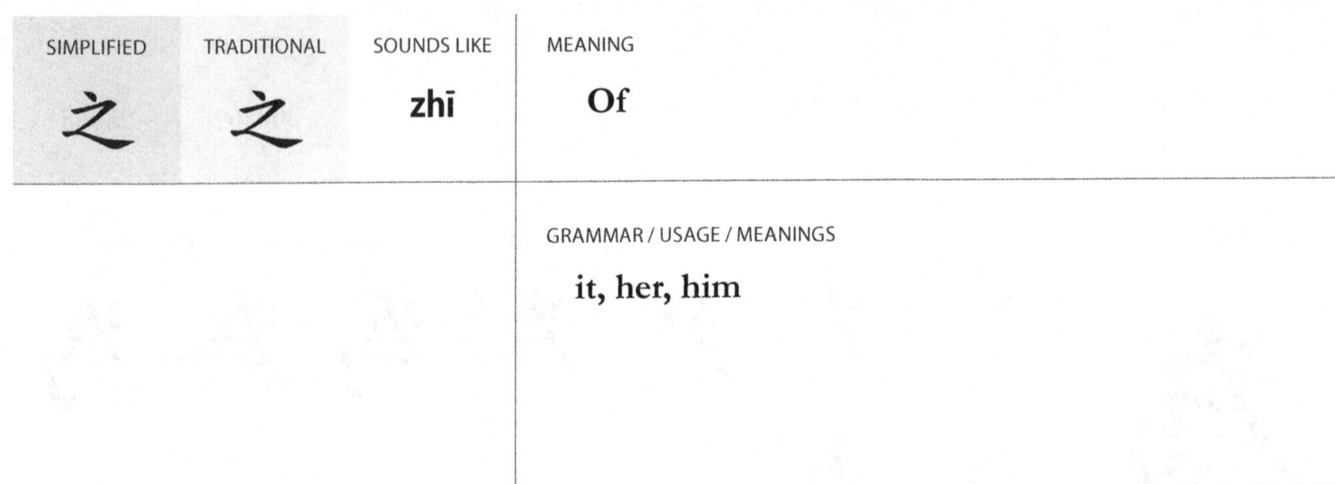

SIMPLIFIED	TRADITIONAL	SOUNDS LIKE	MEANING
之	之	zhī	**Of**

GRAMMAR / USAGE / MEANINGS

it, her, him

SIMPLIFIED   WRITE   trace and draw this letter in the cells below

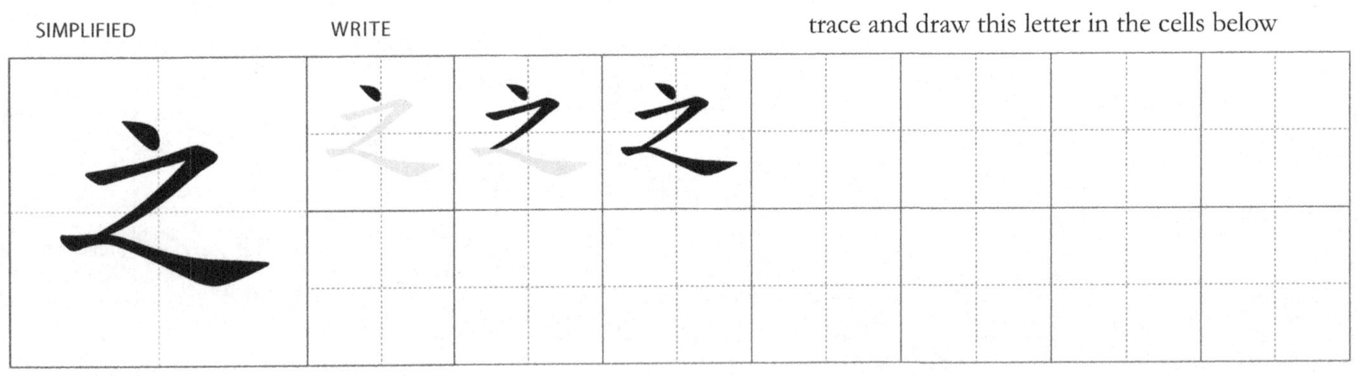

LEARN

UNICODE SIM.	UNICODE TRAD.
20043	20043

TRADITIONAL

之

WRITE

trace and draw this letter in the cells below

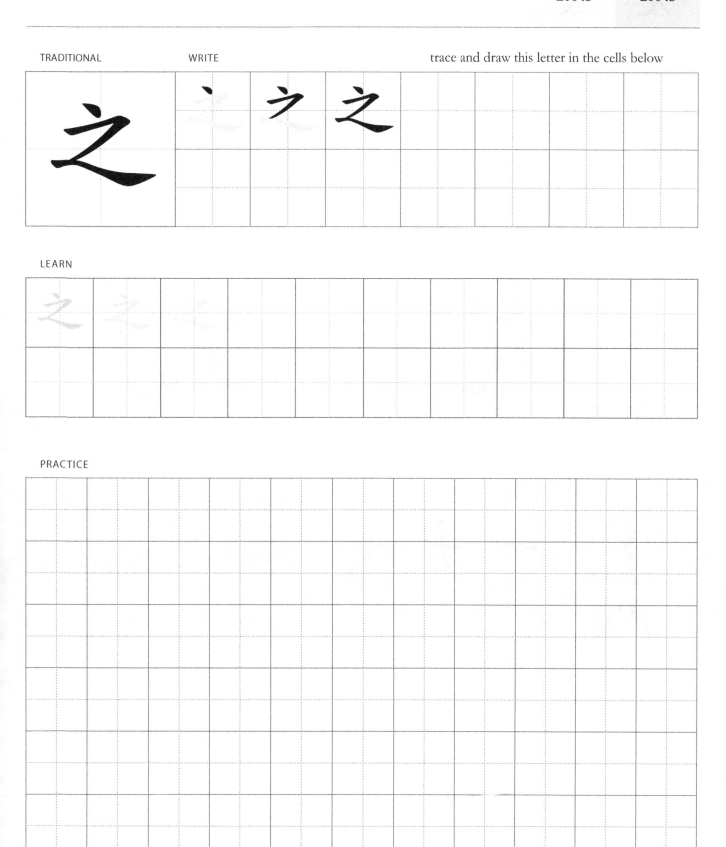

LEARN

PRACTICE

SIMPLIFIED	TRADITIONAL	SOUNDS LIKE	MEANING
大	大	dà	Big

GRAMMAR / USAGE / MEANINGS

eldest / doctor, big, large, strong, heary, major, huge, great, wide, oldest, deep

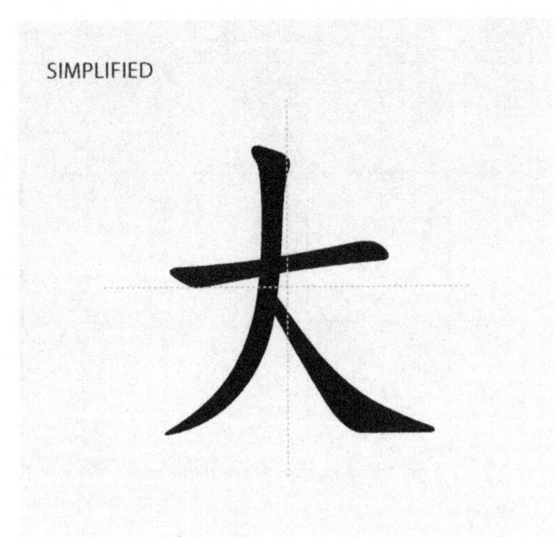

SIMPLIFIED

TRADITIONAL

SIMPLIFIED

大

WRITE

trace and draw this letter in the cells below

LEARN

UNICODE SIM.	UNICODE TRAD.
22823	22823

TRADITIONAL

大

WRITE

trace and draw this letter in the cells below

一 ナ 大

LEARN

大 大 大

PRACTICE

SIMPLIFIED	TRADITIONAL	SOUNDS LIKE	MEANING
来	来	lái	Come

GRAMMAR / USAGE / MEANINGS

to come

TRADITIONAL

来

SIMPLIFIED WRITE trace and draw this letter in the cells below

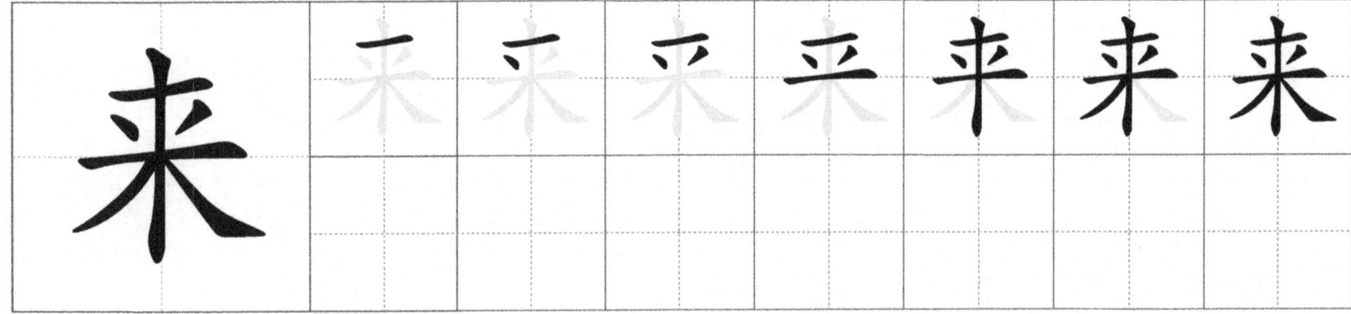

LEARN

UNICODE SIM.	UNICODE TRAD.
26469	20358

TRADITIONAL

來

WRITE

trace and draw this letter in the cells below

一 丆 丆 丆 丆 朩 來 來

LEARN

来 来

PRACTICE

SIMPLIFIED	TRADITIONAL	SOUNDS LIKE	MEANING
以	以	yǐ	With

GRAMMAR / USAGE / MEANINGS

according to, in order to, because of, to use, take

SIMPLIFIED

TRADITIONAL

SIMPLIFIED

以

WRITE

trace and draw this letter in the cells below

LEARN

UNICODE SIM.	UNICODE TRAD.
20197	20197

TRADITIONAL

以

WRITE

trace and draw this letter in the cells below

LEARN

PRACTICE

SIMPLIFIED	TRADITIONAL	SOUNDS LIKE	MEANING
个	個	**gè**	**Individual**

GRAMMAR / USAGE / MEANINGS

individual (a measure word)

SIMPLIFIED

个

TRADITIONAL

個

SIMPLIFIED WRITE trace and draw this letter in the cells below

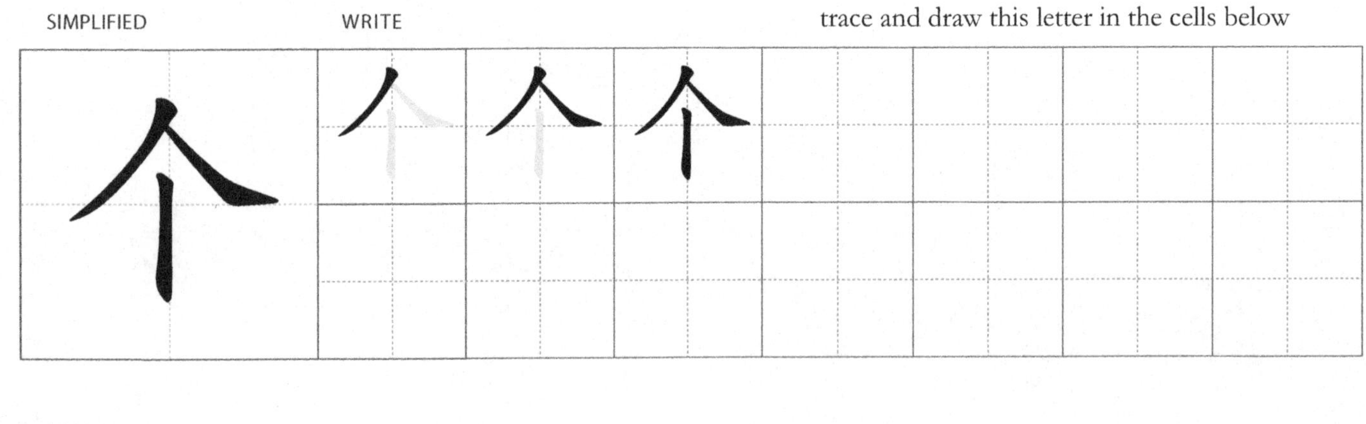

LEARN

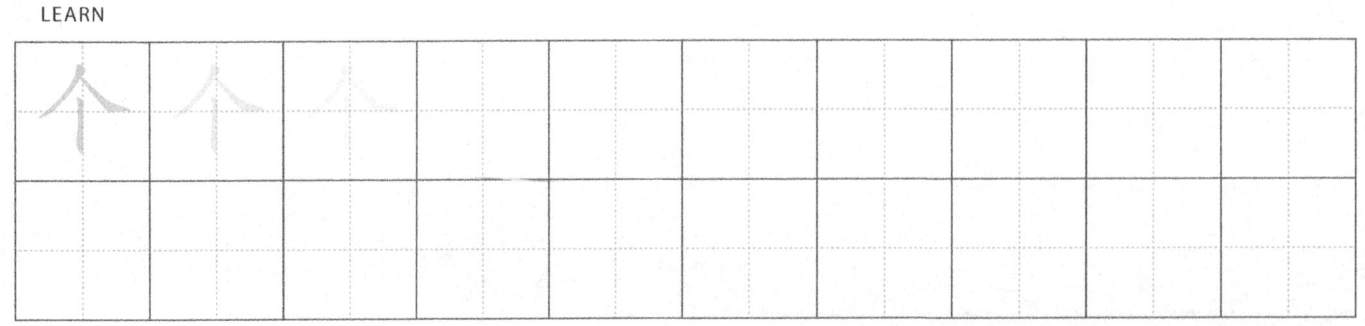

UNICODE SIM.	UNICODE TRAD.
20010	20491

TRADITIONAL

個

WRITE

trace and draw this letter in the cells below

LEARN

PRACTICE

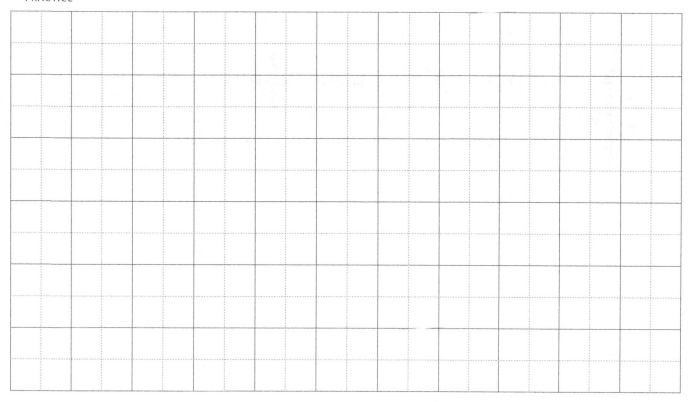

SIMPLIFIED	TRADITIONAL	SOUNDS LIKE	MEANING
中	中	zhōng	Middle

GRAMMAR / USAGE / MEANINGS

among, within, in, middle, medium, center, during, while (doing something)

SIMPLIFIED

中

WRITE

trace and draw this letter in the cells below

LEARN

UNICODE SIM.	UNICODE TRAD.
20013	20013

TRADITIONAL

中

WRITE

trace and draw this letter in the cells below

丨 ⼌ 口 中

LEARN

中 中

PRACTICE

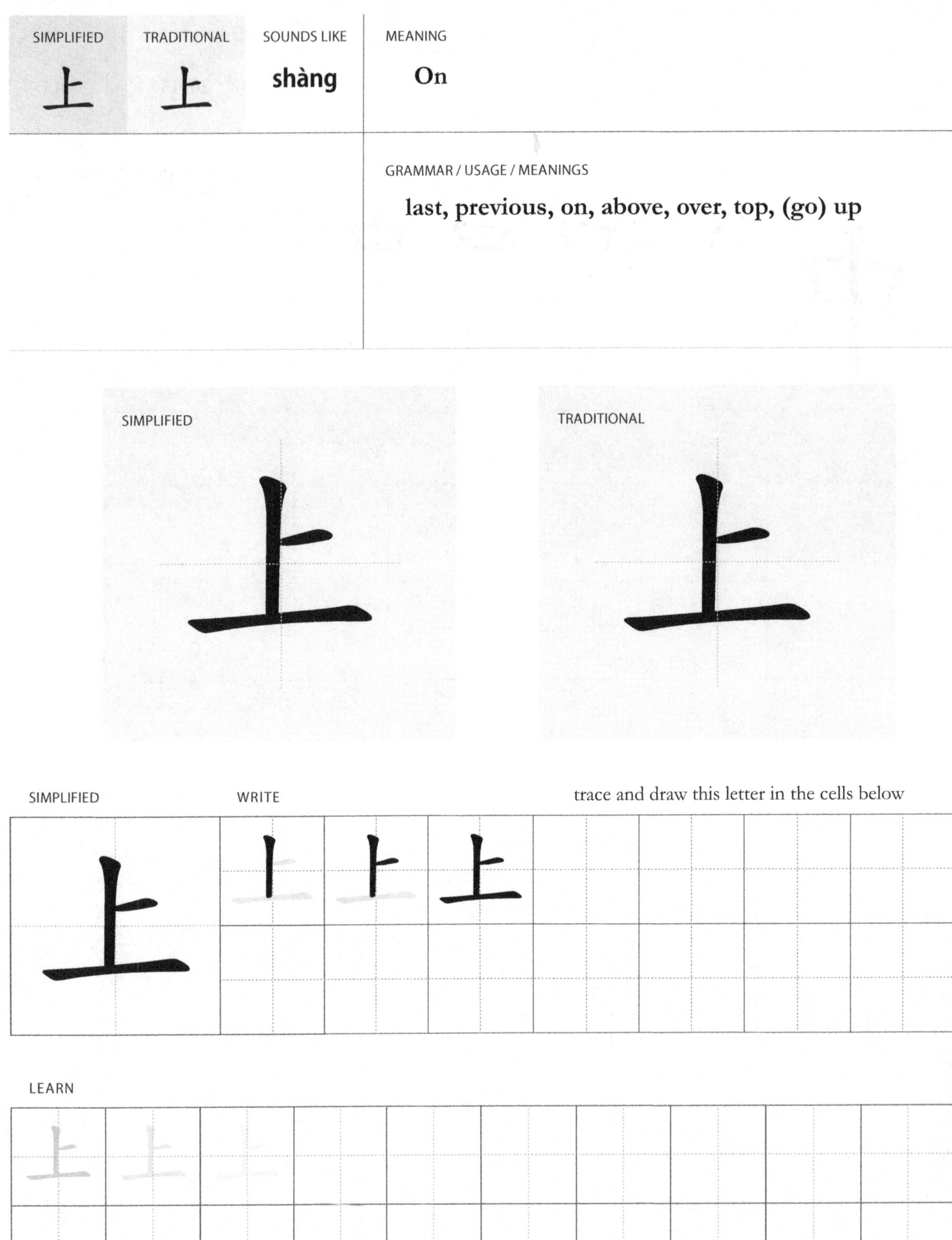

SIMPLIFIED	TRADITIONAL	SOUNDS LIKE	MEANING
上	上	**shàng**	**On**

GRAMMAR / USAGE / MEANINGS

last, previous, on, above, over, top, (go) up

SIMPLIFIED

上

TRADITIONAL

上

SIMPLIFIED

上

WRITE

trace and draw this letter in the cells below

LEARN

UNICODE SIM.	UNICODE TRAD.
19978	19978

TRADITIONAL

上

WRITE

丨 ⺊ 上

trace and draw this letter in the cells below

LEARN

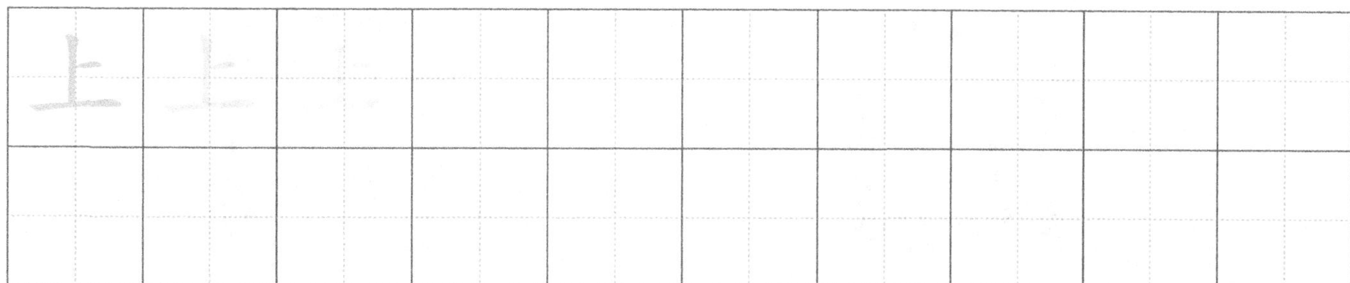

PRACTICE

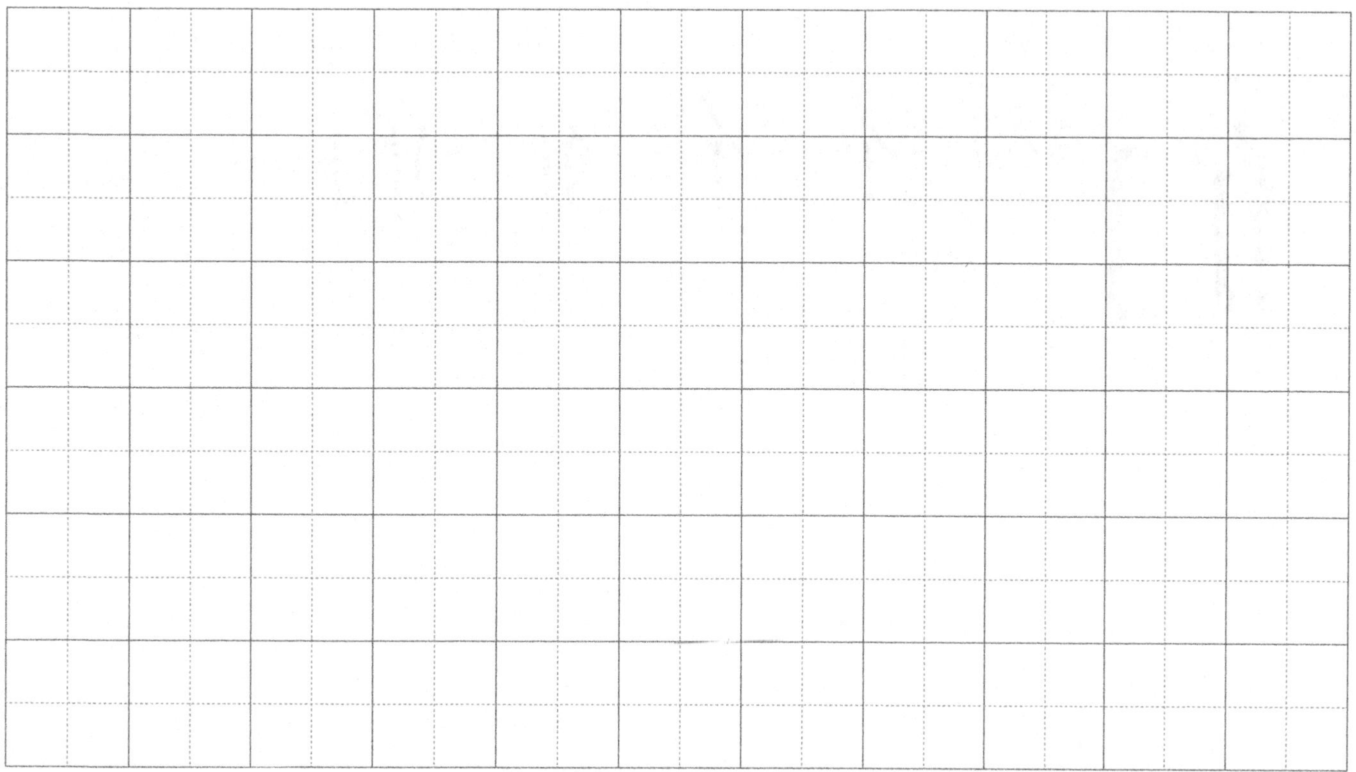

SIMPLIFIED	TRADITIONAL	SOUNDS LIKE	MEANING
们	們	men	We

GRAMMAR / USAGE / MEANINGS

(a few animate nouns and plural marker for pronouns)

SIMPLIFIED

们

TRADITIONAL

們

SIMPLIFIED

WRITE

trace and draw this letter in the cells below

LEARN

UNICODE SIM.	UNICODE TRAD.
20204	**20497**

TRADITIONAL

們

WRITE

trace and draw this letter in the cells below

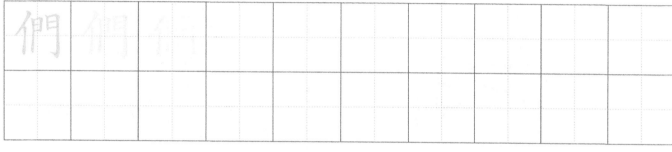

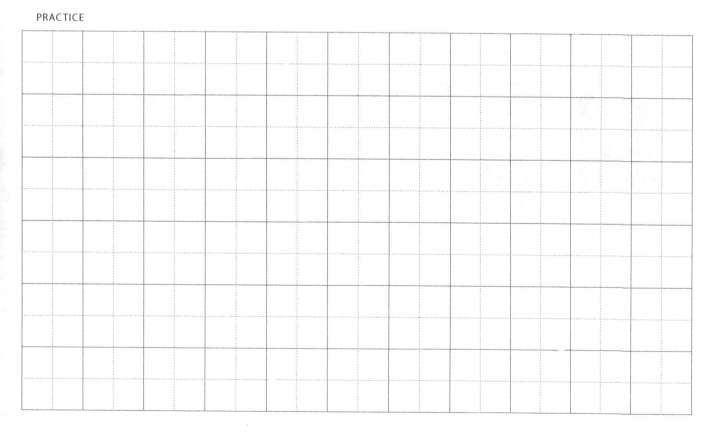

LEARN

PRACTICE

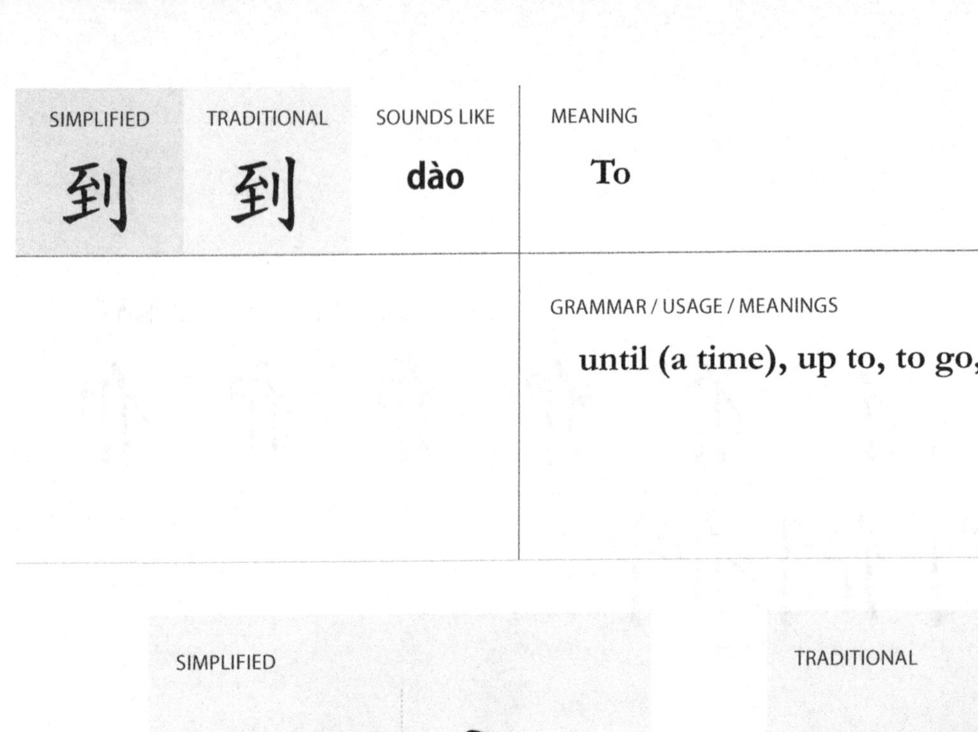

SIMPLIFIED	TRADITIONAL	SOUNDS LIKE	MEANING
到	到	dào	To

GRAMMAR / USAGE / MEANINGS

until (a time), up to, to go, to arrive, to (a place)

SIMPLIFIED

到

WRITE

trace and draw this letter in the cells below

LEARN

UNICODE SIM.	UNICODE TRAD.
21040	21040

TRADITIONAL

到

WRITE

trace and draw this letter in the cells below

一 　 　 　 　 　 至 到 到

LEARN

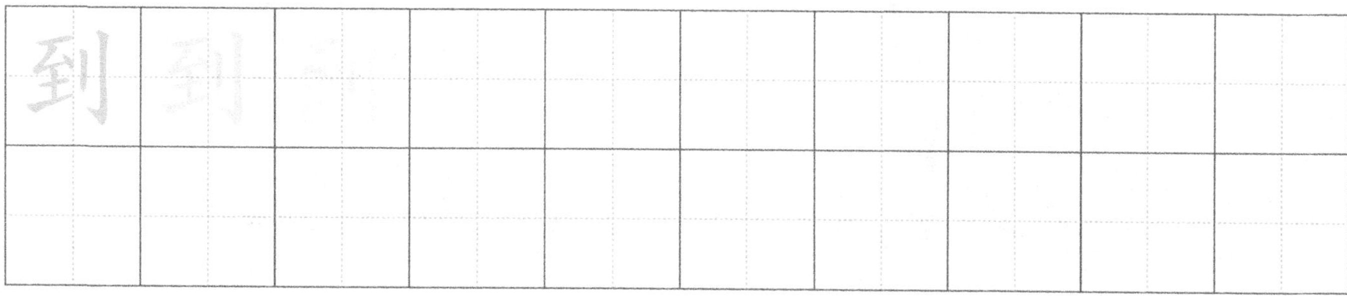

PRACTICE

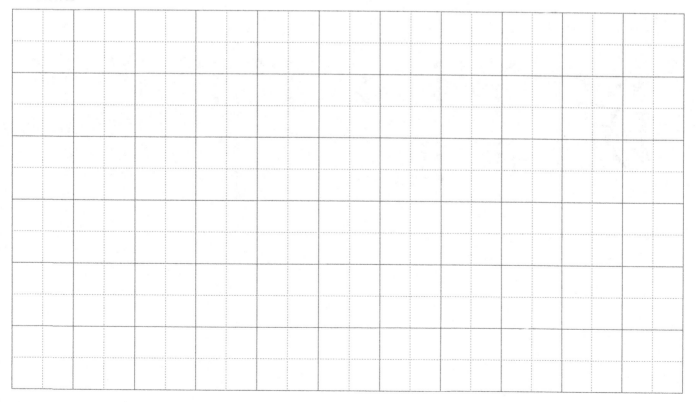

SIMPLIFIED	TRADITIONAL	SOUNDS LIKE	MEANING
说	說	**shuō**	**Says**

GRAMMAR / USAGE / MEANINGS

to say, to explain, to criticize, to speak

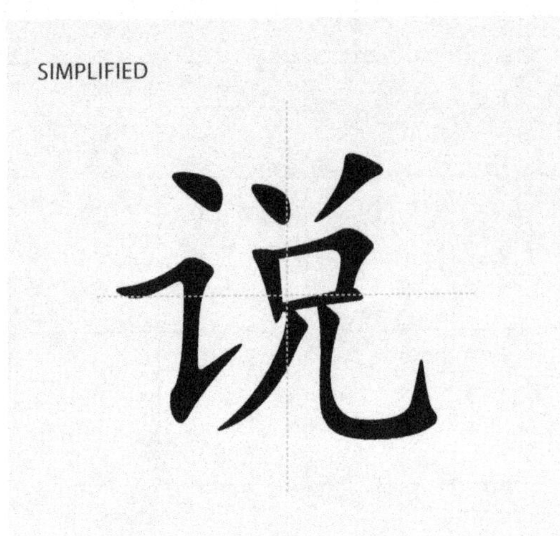

TRADITIONAL

說

SIMPLIFIED WRITE trace and draw this letter in the cells below

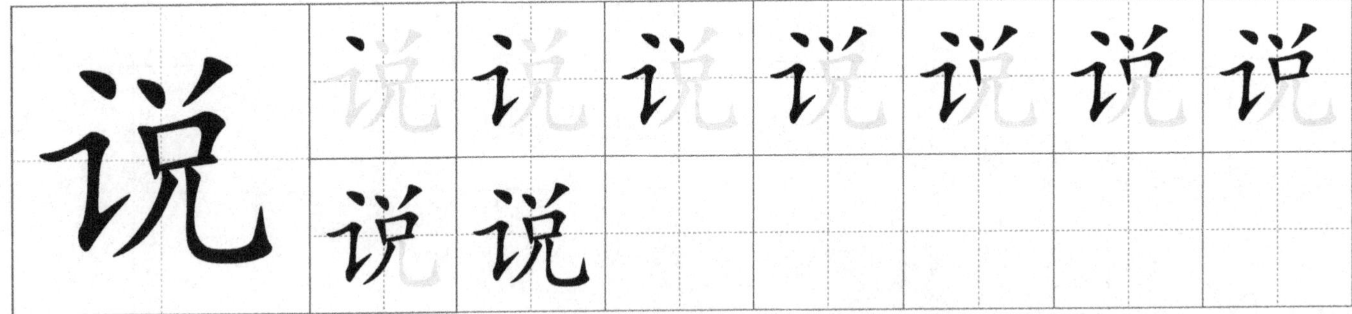

LEARN

UNICODE SIM.	UNICODE TRAD.
35828	35500

TRADITIONAL

說

WRITE

trace and draw this letter in the cells below

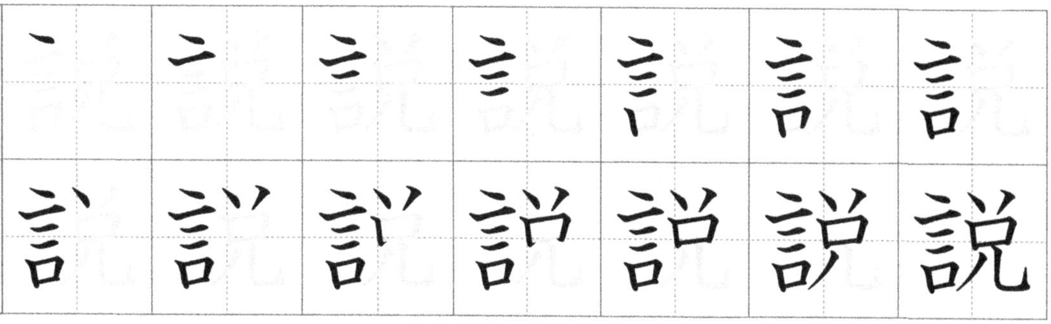

LEARN

PRACTICE

SIMPLIFIED	TRADITIONAL	SOUNDS LIKE	MEANING
		**guó**	Country

GRAMMAR / USAGE / MEANINGS

country, state, national, nation

SIMPLIFIED

TRADITIONAL

SIMPLIFIED | WRITE | trace and draw this letter in the cells below

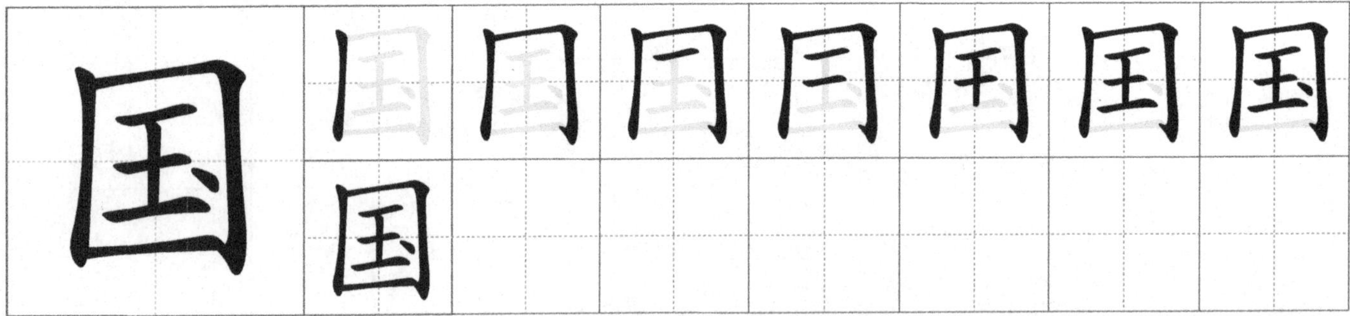

LEARN

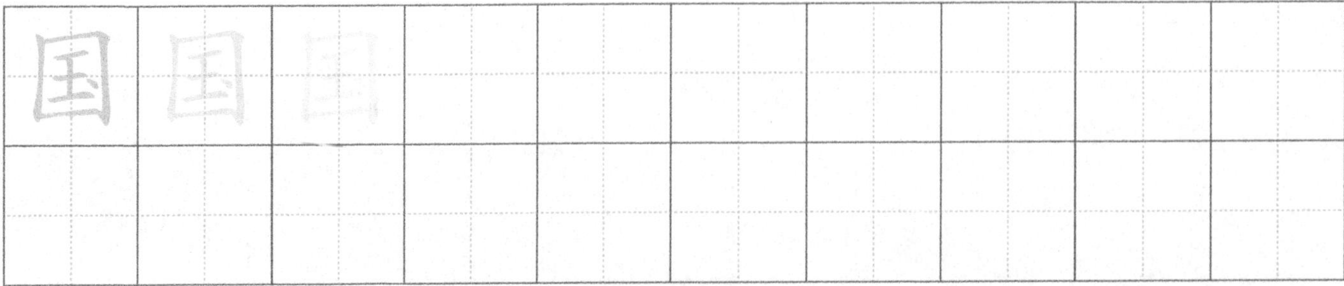

UNICODE SIM.	UNICODE TRAD.
22269	22283

TRADITIONAL

WRITE

trace and draw this letter in the cells below

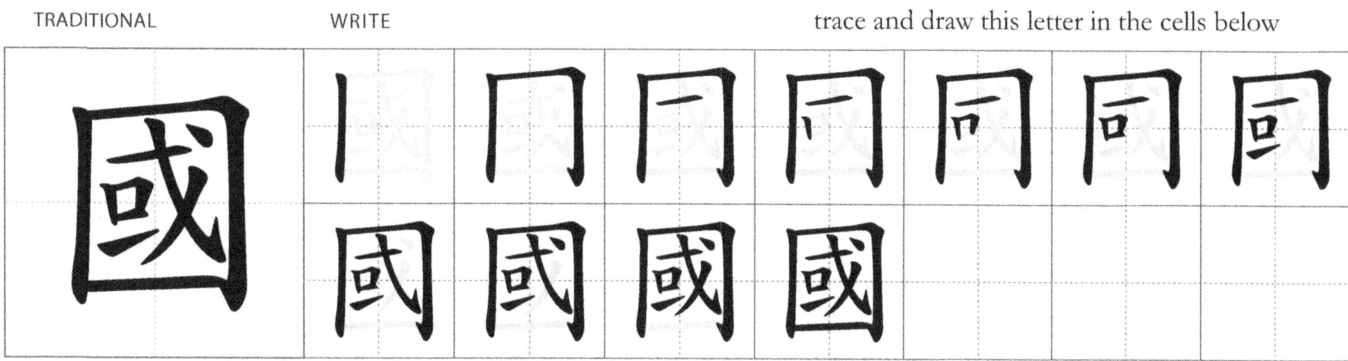

LEARN

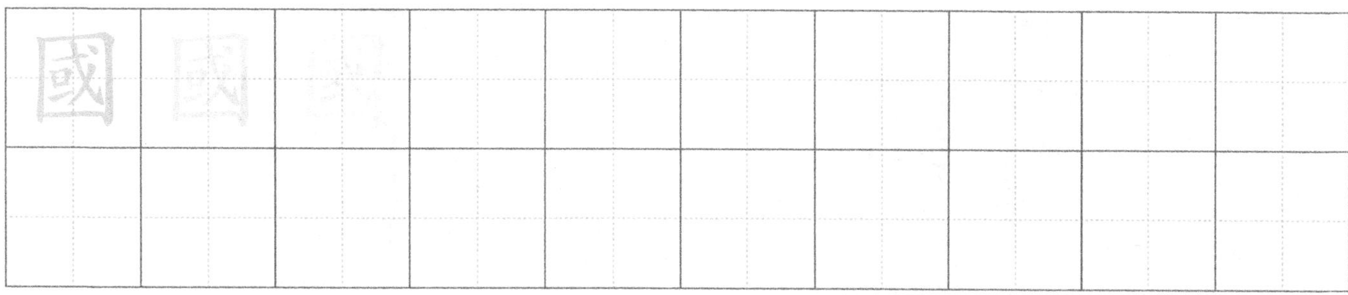

PRACTICE

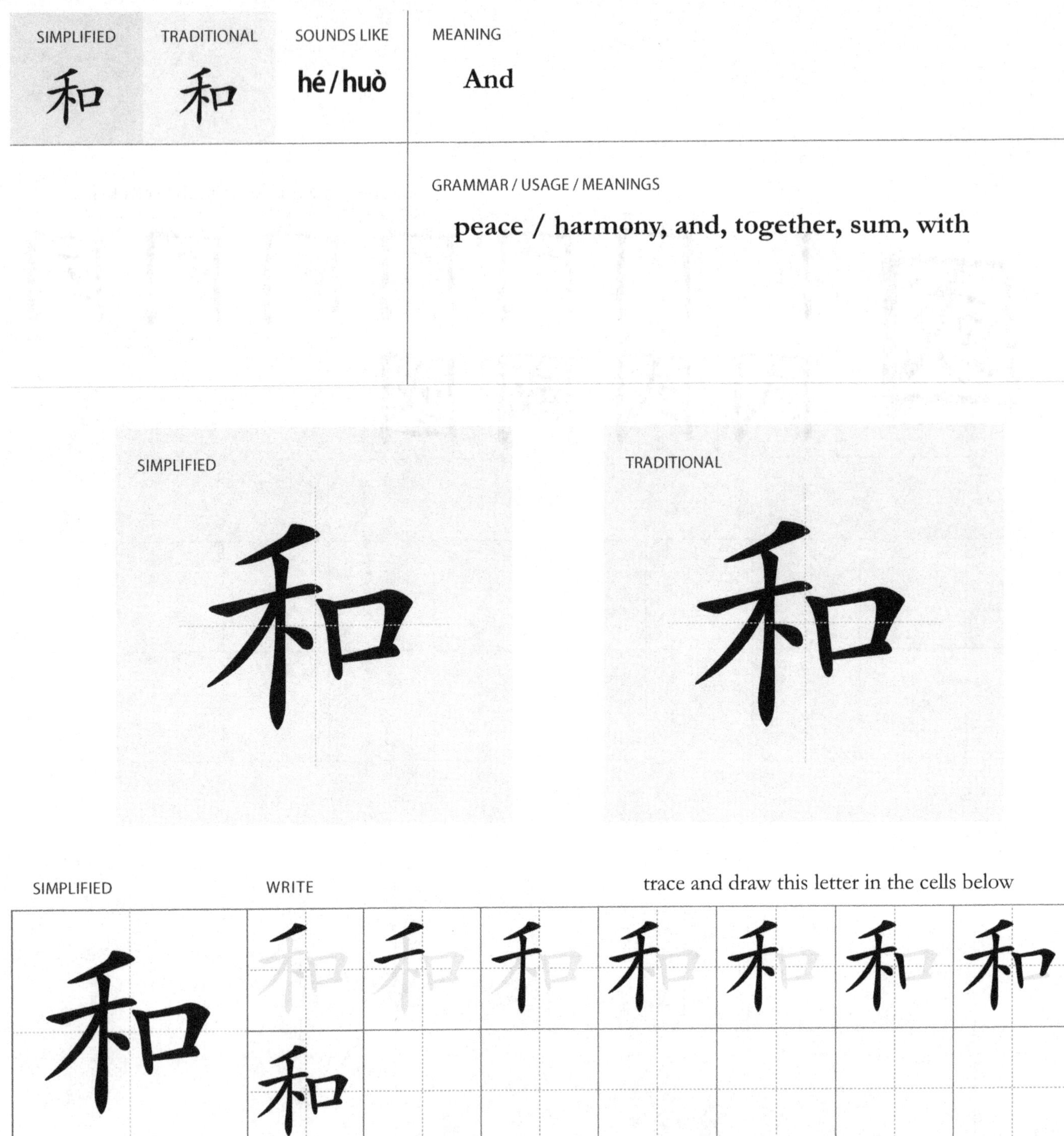

SIMPLIFIED	TRADITIONAL	SOUNDS LIKE	MEANING
和	和	**hé / huò**	**And**

GRAMMAR / USAGE / MEANINGS

peace / harmony, and, together, sum, with

SIMPLIFIED

WRITE

trace and draw this letter in the cells below

和

和 和 和 和 和 和 和 和

LEARN

和 和 和

UNICODE SIM.	UNICODE TRAD.
21644	21644

TRADITIONAL

和

WRITE

trace and draw this letter in the cells below

LEARN

PRACTICE

SIMPLIFIED	TRADITIONAL	SOUNDS LIKE	MEANING
地	地	de / dì	Ground

GRAMMAR / USAGE / MEANINGS

/ly / earth, place, land, ground, field

SIMPLIFIED

地

TRADITIONAL

地

SIMPLIFIED

WRITE

trace and draw this letter in the cells below

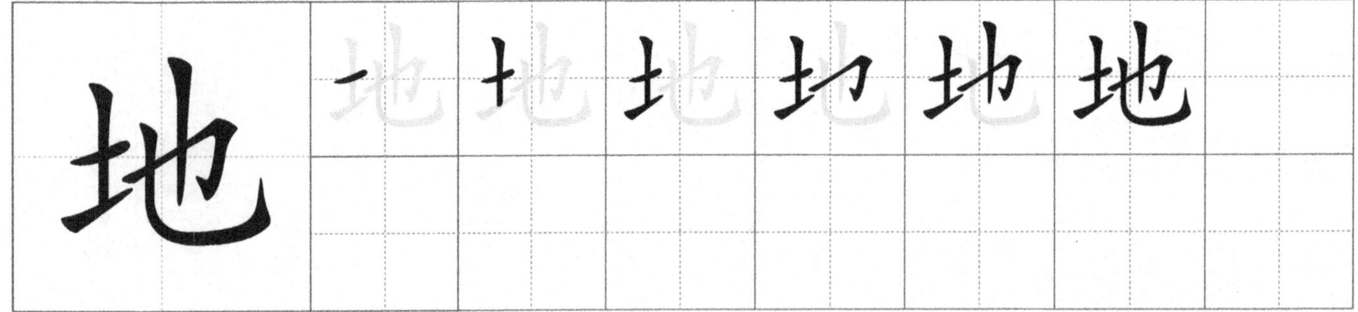

LEARN

UNICODE SIM.	UNICODE TRAD.
22320	22320

TRADITIONAL

地

WRITE

trace and draw this letter in the cells below

一 十 土 圵 圵 地

LEARN

地 地 地

PRACTICE

SIMPLIFIED	TRADITIONAL	SOUNDS LIKE	MEANING
也	也	yě	**Also**

GRAMMAR / USAGE / MEANINGS

as well, too, also

SIMPLIFIED

也

TRADITIONAL

也

SIMPLIFIED　　WRITE　　trace and draw this letter in the cells below

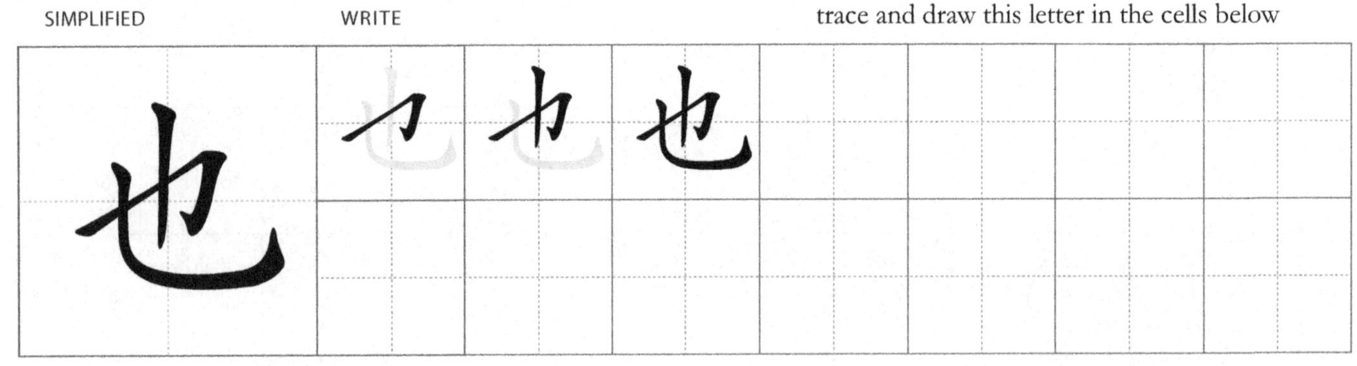

LEARN

也 也 也

UNICODE SIM.	UNICODE TRAD.
20063	20063

TRADITIONAL

也

WRITE

trace and draw this letter in the cells below

LEARN

PRACTICE

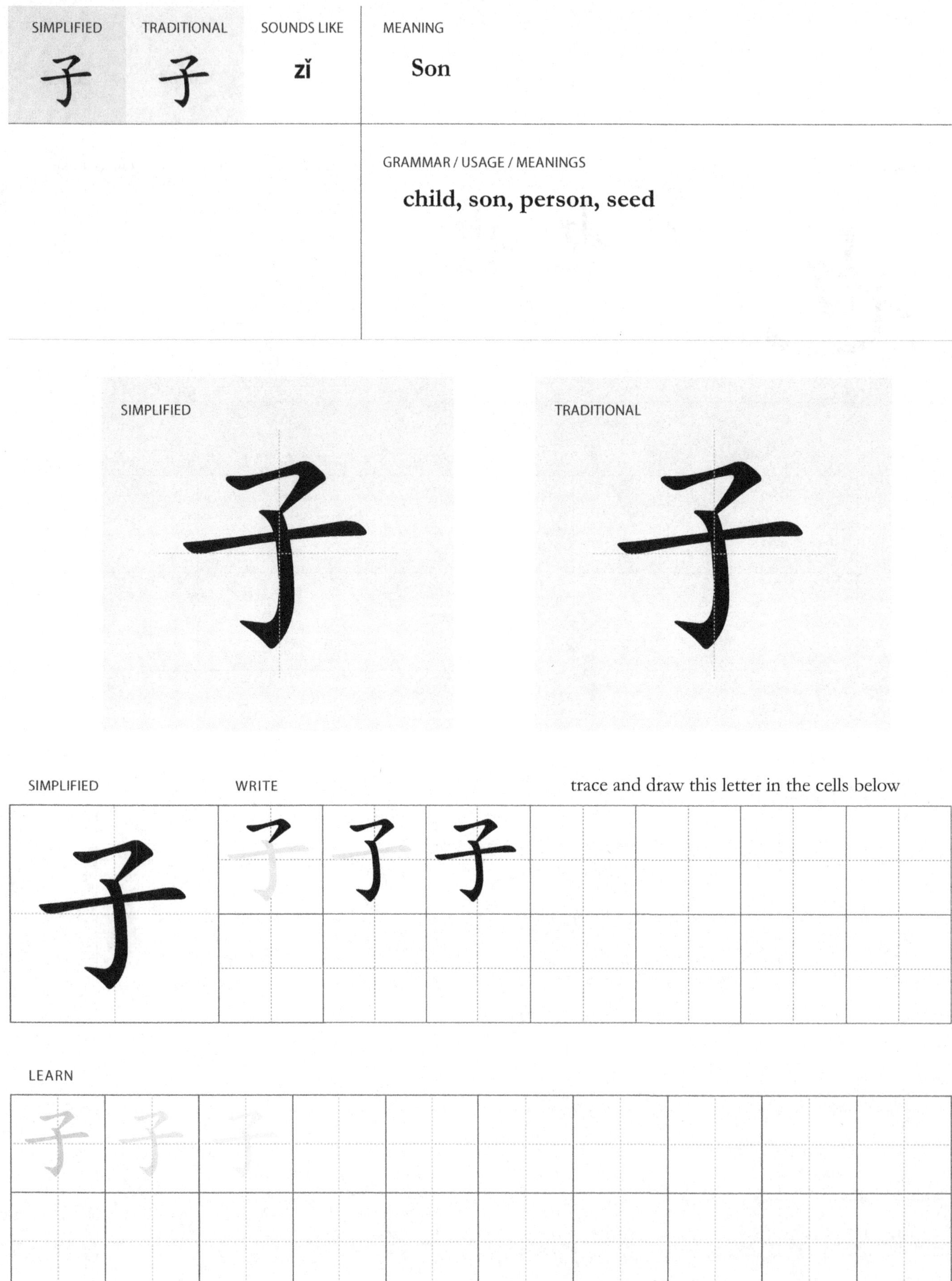
SIMPLIFIED
子
TRADITIONAL
子
SOUNDS LIKE
zǐ
MEANING
Son
GRAMMAR / USAGE / MEANINGS
child, son, person, seed
SIMPLIFIED
子
TRADITIONAL
子
SIMPLIFIED
WRITE
trace and draw this letter in the cells below
LEARN

UNICODE SIM.	UNICODE TRAD.
23376	**23376**

TRADITIONAL

子

WRITE

trace and draw this letter in the cells below

LEARN

PRACTICE

SIMPLIFIED	TRADITIONAL	SOUNDS LIKE	MEANING
时	時	shí	Time

GRAMMAR / USAGE / MEANINGS

when, period, season, time, hour

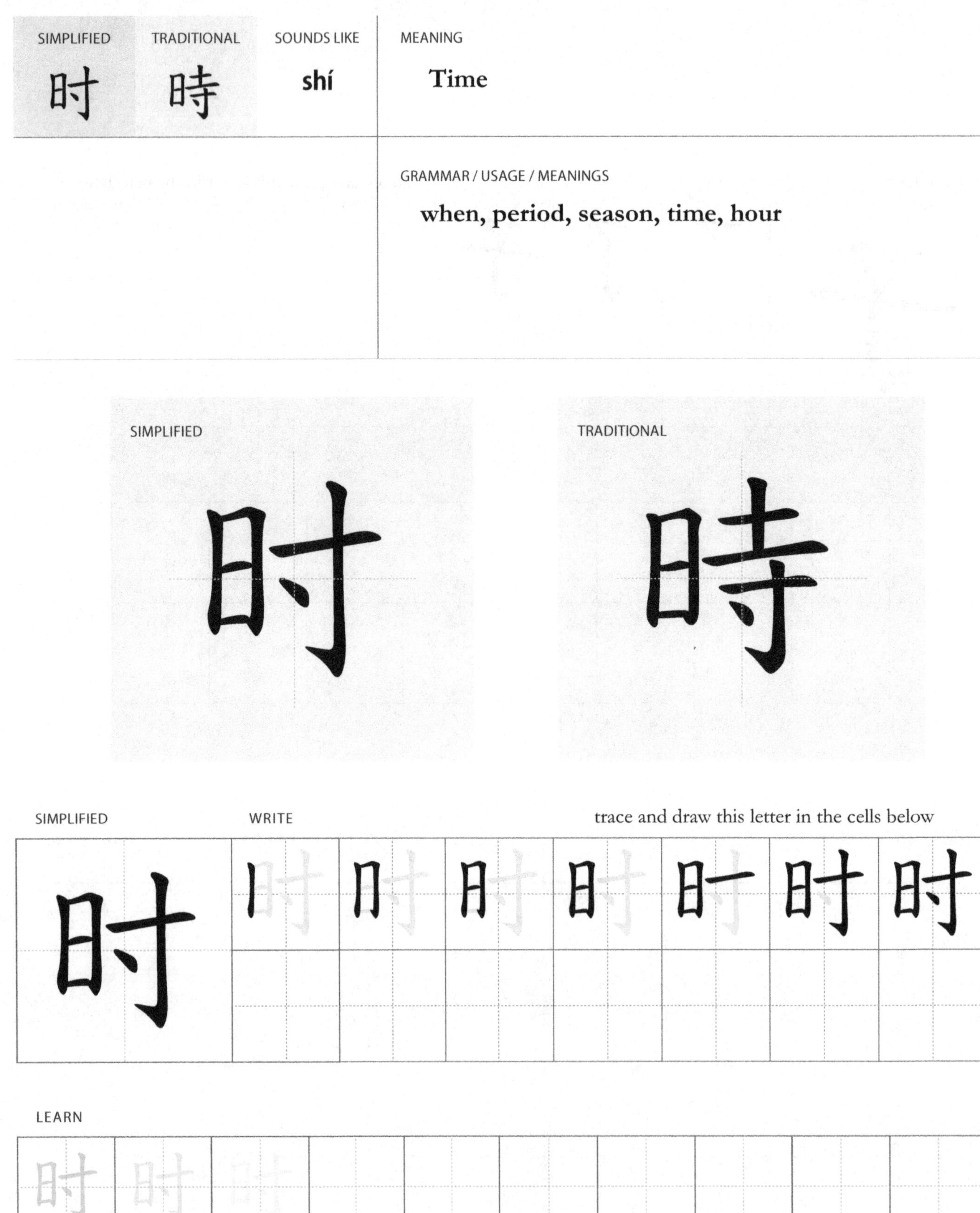

UNICODE SIM.	UNICODE TRAD.
26102	26178

TRADITIONAL

時

WRITE

trace and draw this letter in the cells below

丨 冂 日 日 日一 日十 日土 日圭 時 時

LEARN

時 時

PRACTICE

SIMPLIFIED	TRADITIONAL	SOUNDS LIKE	MEANING
道	道	dào	Road

GRAMMAR / USAGE / MEANINGS

method, a measure word, reason, to say, to speak, to talk, direction, way, method, road, path, principle, truth, skill, Tao (of Taoism)

SIMPLIFIED

道

TRADITIONAL

道

SIMPLIFIED

道

WRITE

trace and draw this letter in the cells below

LEARN

道 道 道

UNICODE SIM.	UNICODE TRAD.
36947	36947

TRADITIONAL

WRITE

trace and draw this letter in the cells below

道

丶 丷 䒑 䒑 䒑 𫇦 𫇦 首 首 道 道 道

LEARN

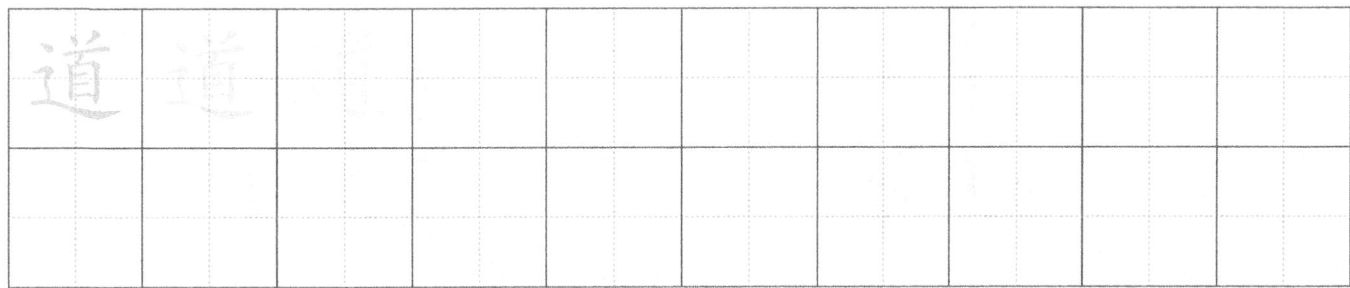

PRACTICE

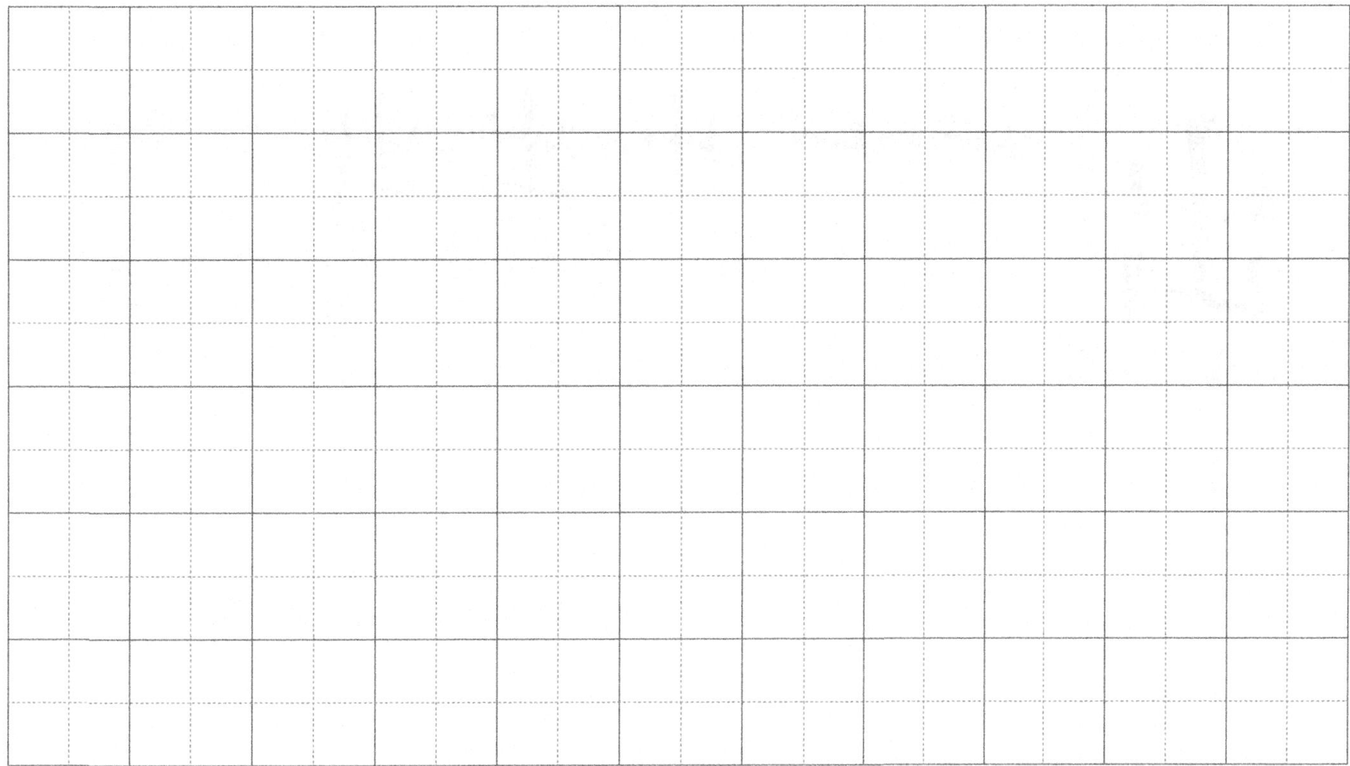

SIMPLIFIED	TRADITIONAL	SOUNDS LIKE	MEANING
出	出	chū	Out

GRAMMAR / USAGE / MEANINGS

to rise, to put forth, to occur, to happen, to go out, to come out, to occur, to produce, to go beyond

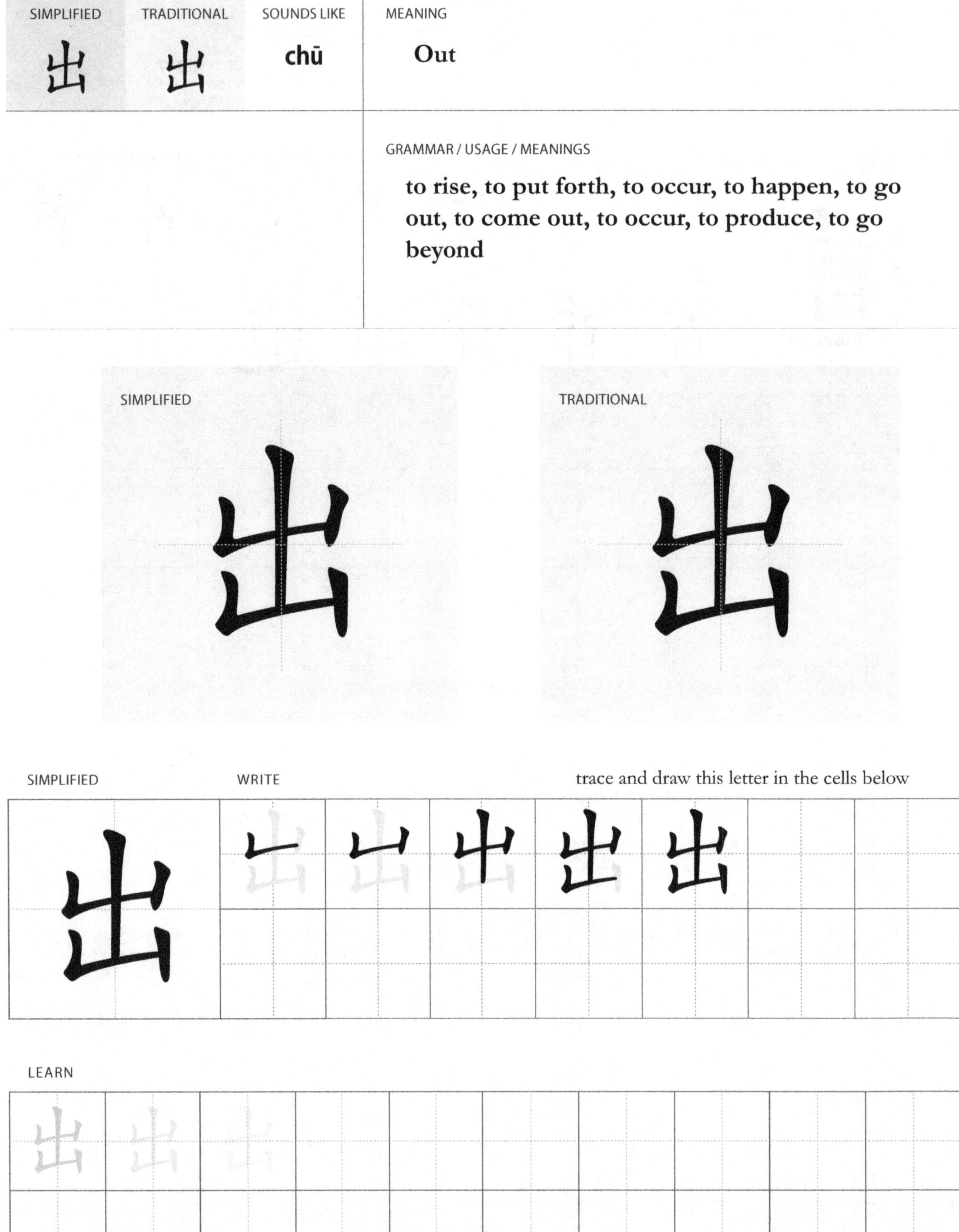

UNICODE SIM.	UNICODE TRAD.
20986	**20986**

TRADITIONAL

出

WRITE

trace and draw this letter in the cells below

LEARN

PRACTICE

SIMPLIFIED	TRADITIONAL	SOUNDS LIKE	MEANING
而	而	ér	And

GRAMMAR / USAGE / MEANINGS

(shows change of state), (shows causal relation), (shows contrast) and, as well as, but (not), yet (not),

SIMPLIFIED

而

TRADITIONAL

而

SIMPLIFIED

WRITE

trace and draw this letter in the cells below

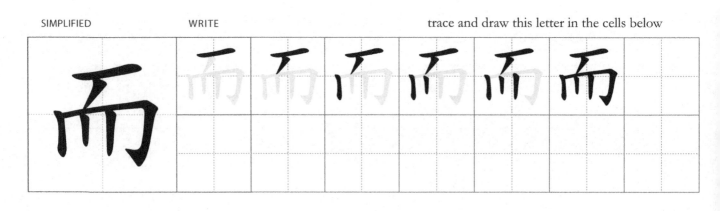

而

LEARN

UNICODE SIM.	UNICODE TRAD.
32780	**32780**

TRADITIONAL

而

WRITE

trace and draw this letter in the cells below

LEARN

PRACTICE

SIMPLIFIED	TRADITIONAL	SOUNDS LIKE	MEANING
要	要	yào/yāo	Want

GRAMMAR / USAGE / MEANINGS

must / demand, ask, to be going to, request, vital, to want

SIMPLIFIED

要

TRADITIONAL

要

SIMPLIFIED

WRITE

trace and draw this letter in the cells below

LEARN

UNICODE SIM.	UNICODE TRAD.
35201	**35201**

TRADITIONAL

要

WRITE

trace and draw this letter in the cells below

要 要

LEARN

要 要

PRACTICE

SIMPLIFIED	TRADITIONAL	SOUNDS LIKE	MEANING
于	於 OR 于	**yú**	**At**

GRAMMAR / USAGE / MEANINGS

in regard to, at, in

SIMPLIFIED

于

TRADITIONAL

於 OR 于

于 于 于 于

于 于 于

UNICODE SIM.	UNICODE TRAD.
20110	26044 or 20110

於

亍 方 方 方 於 於 於

于

一 二 于

LEARN

於 於 於

于 于 于

PRACTICE

SIMPLIFIED	TRADITIONAL	SOUNDS LIKE	MEANING
就	就	jiù	**Just**

GRAMMAR / USAGE / MEANINGS

then, only, just, at once, right away

SIMPLIFIED

TRADITIONAL

就

SIMPLIFIED　　WRITE　　trace and draw this letter in the cells below

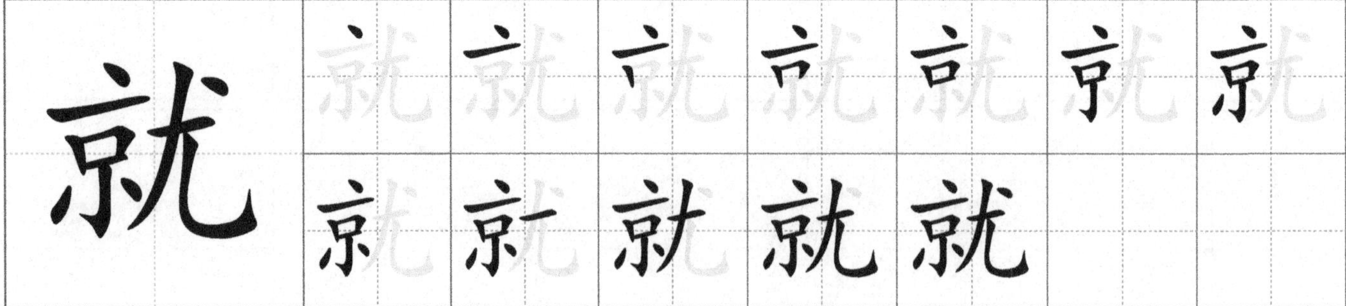

LEARN

UNICODE SIM.	UNICODE TRAD.
23601	23601

TRADITIONAL

就

WRITE

trace and draw this letter in the cells below

LEARN

PRACTICE

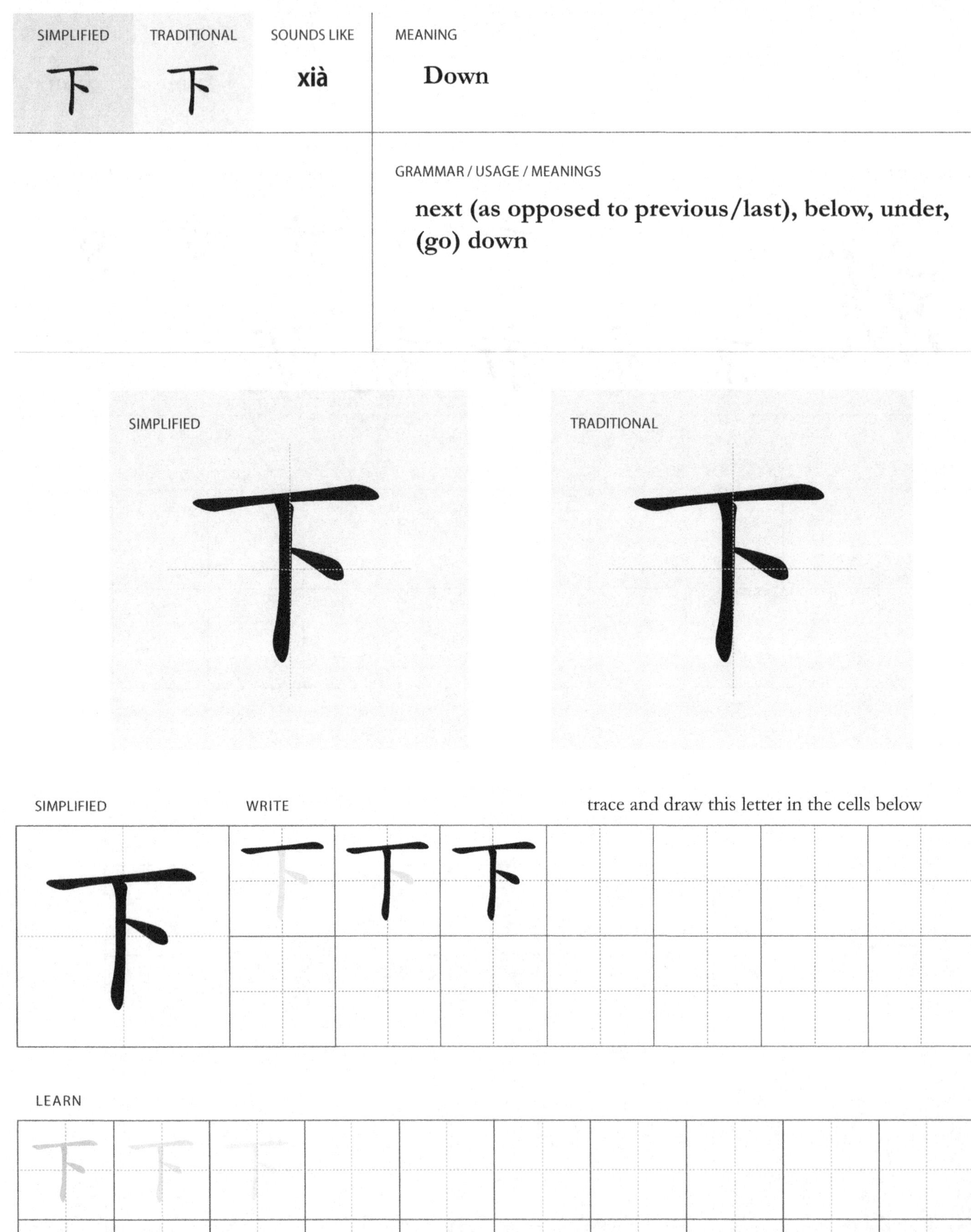

SIMPLIFIED	TRADITIONAL	SOUNDS LIKE	MEANING
下	下	xià	Down

GRAMMAR / USAGE / MEANINGS

next (as opposed to previous/last), below, under, (go) down

SIMPLIFIED

TRADITIONAL

SIMPLIFIED

WRITE

trace and draw this letter in the cells below

LEARN

UNICODE SIM.	UNICODE TRAD.
19979	19979

TRADITIONAL

WRITE

trace and draw this letter in the cells below

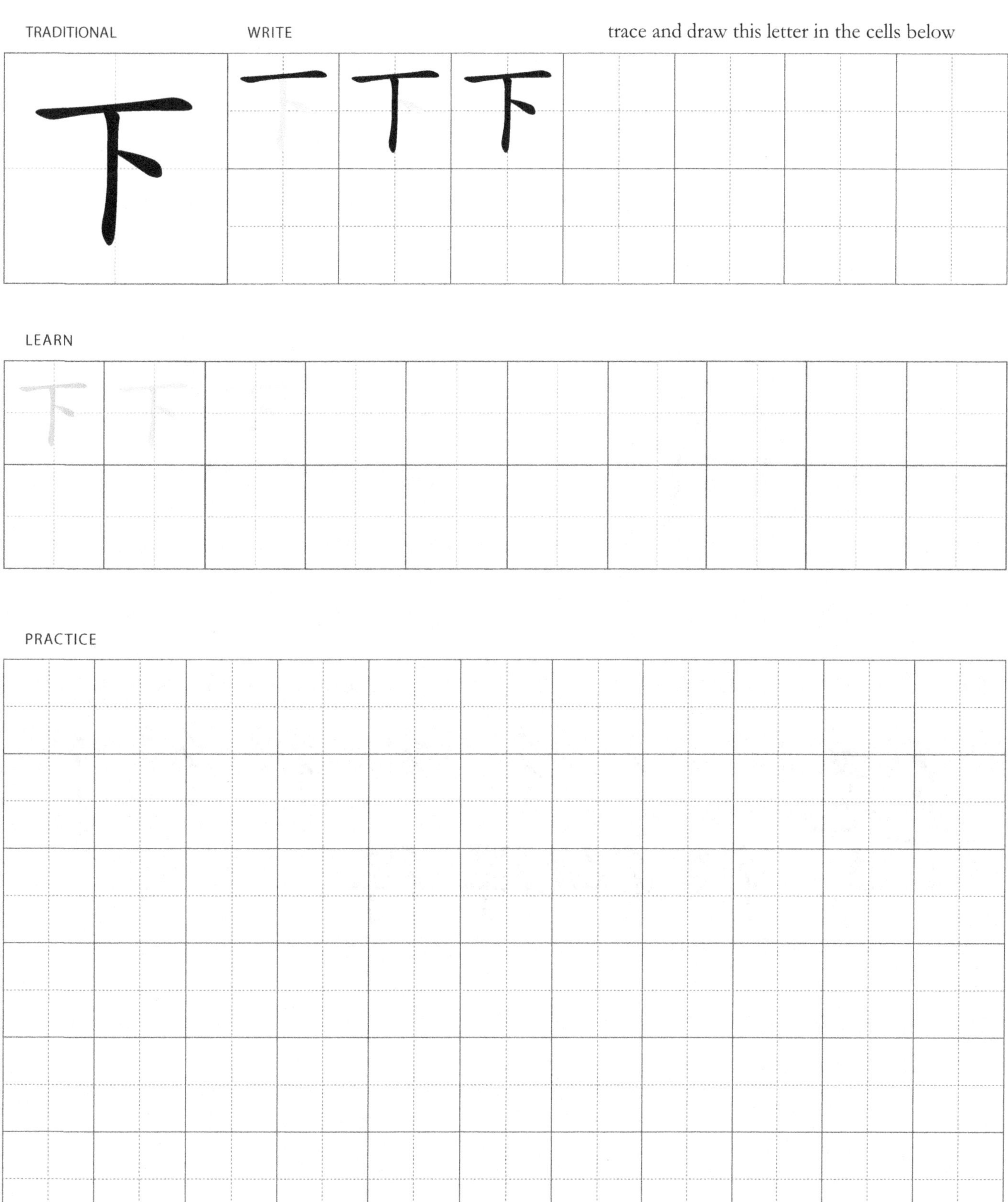

LEARN

PRACTICE

SIMPLIFIED	TRADITIONAL	SOUNDS LIKE	MEANING
得	得	**dé/de/děi**	**Have To**

GRAMMAR / USAGE / MEANINGS

must, get, ought to, obtain, to need to, gain, to have to

SIMPLIFIED

得

TRADITIONAL

得

SIMPLIFIED

WRITE

trace and draw this letter in the cells below

得

LEARN

UNICODE SIM.	UNICODE TRAD.
24471	**24471**

TRADITIONAL

得

WRITE

trace and draw this letter in the cells below

得 得 得 得

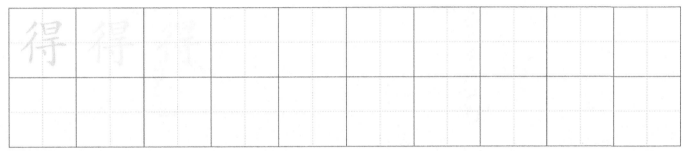

LEARN

PRACTICE

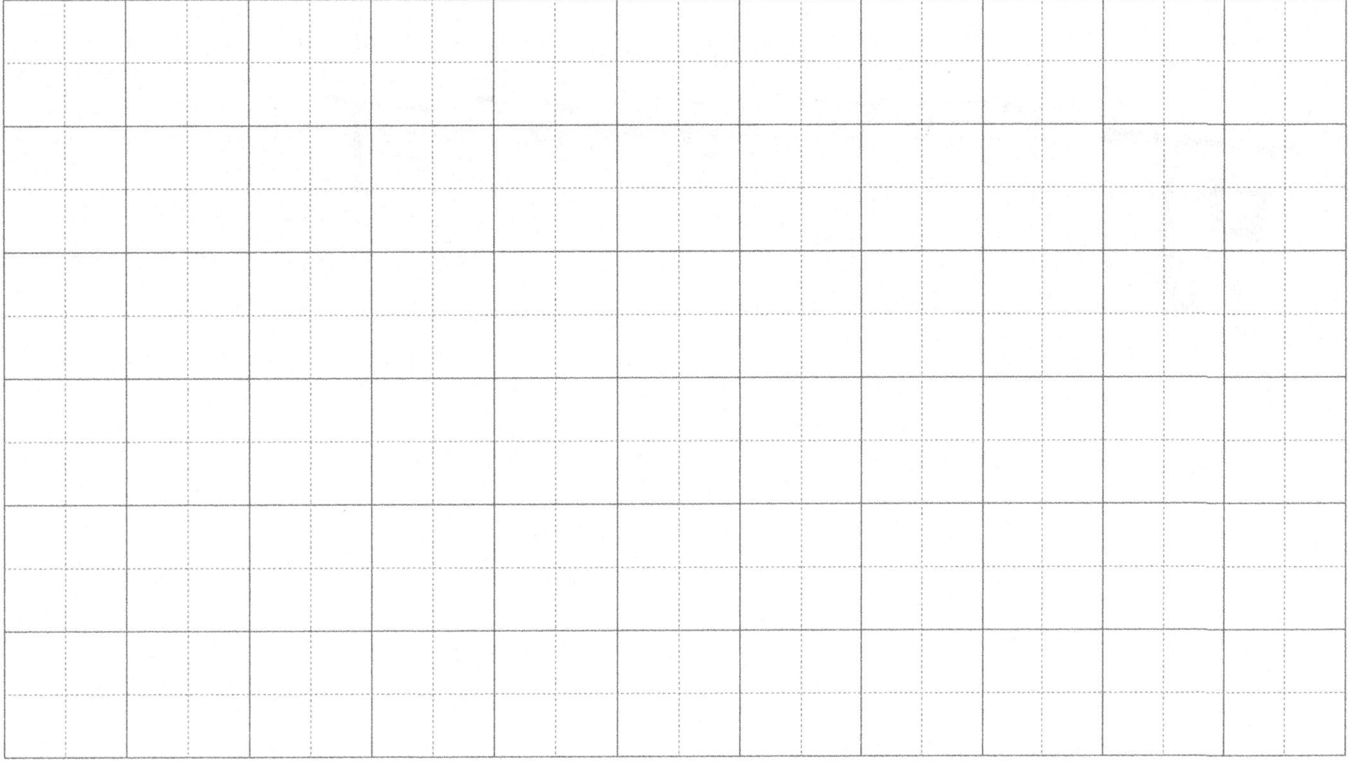

SIMPLIFIED	TRADITIONAL	SOUNDS LIKE	MEANING
可	可	kě	Can

GRAMMAR / USAGE / MEANINGS

(particle used for emphasis), can, may, able to, certain(ly)

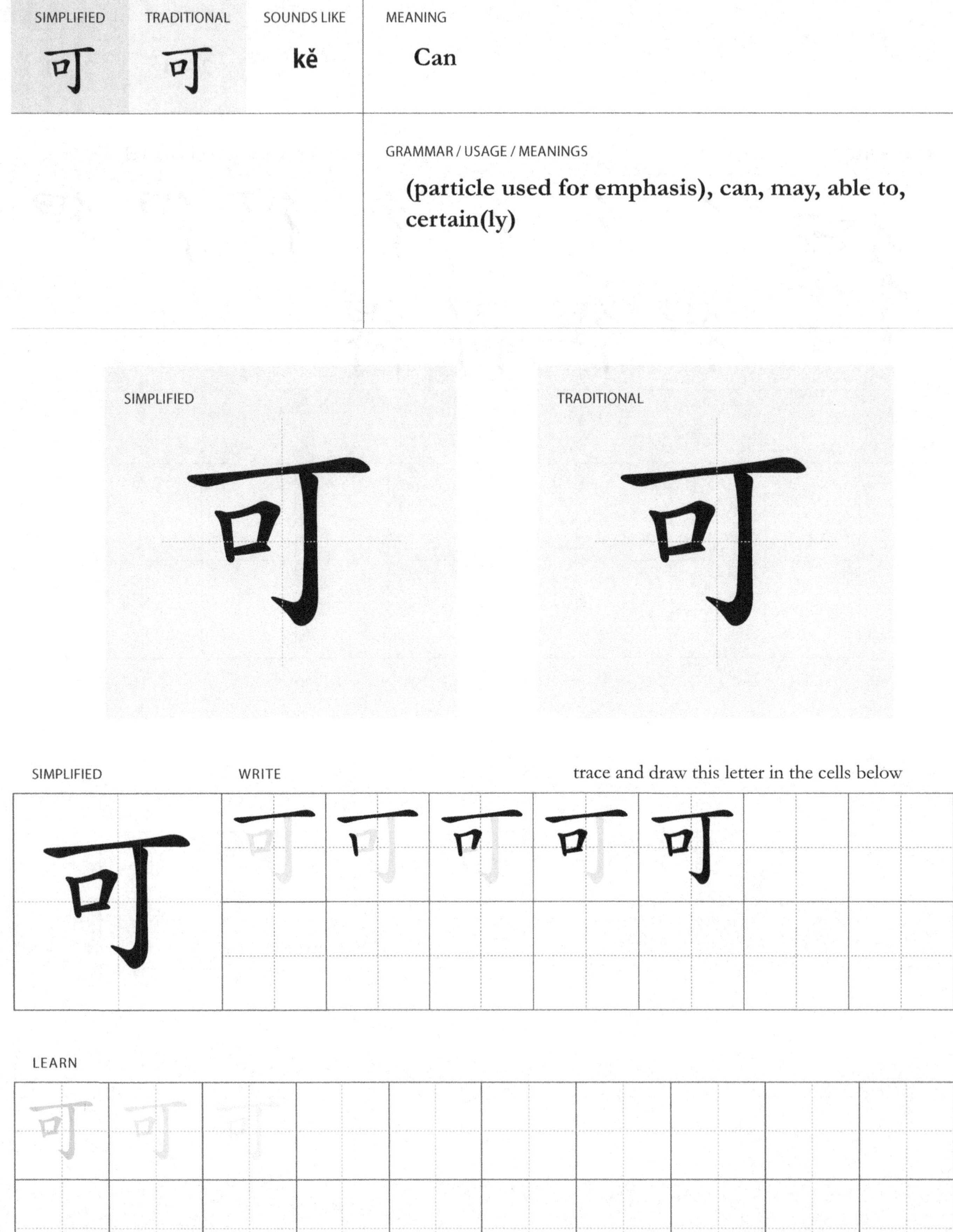

UNICODE SIM.	UNICODE TRAD.
21487	**21487**

TRADITIONAL

可

WRITE

trace and draw this letter in the cells below

LEARN

PRACTICE

SIMPLIFIED	TRADITIONAL	SOUNDS LIKE	MEANING
你	你	nǐ	You

GRAMMAR / USAGE / MEANINGS

you, anyone

SIMPLIFIED

你

TRADITIONAL

你

SIMPLIFIED

你

WRITE

trace and draw this letter in the cells below

LEARN

UNICODE SIM.	UNICODE TRAD.
20320	**20320**

TRADITIONAL

你

WRITE

trace and draw this letter in the cells below

LEARN

你 你

PRACTICE

SIMPLIFIED	TRADITIONAL	SOUNDS LIKE	MEANING
年	年	nián	Year

GRAMMAR / USAGE / MEANINGS

year, New Year, age

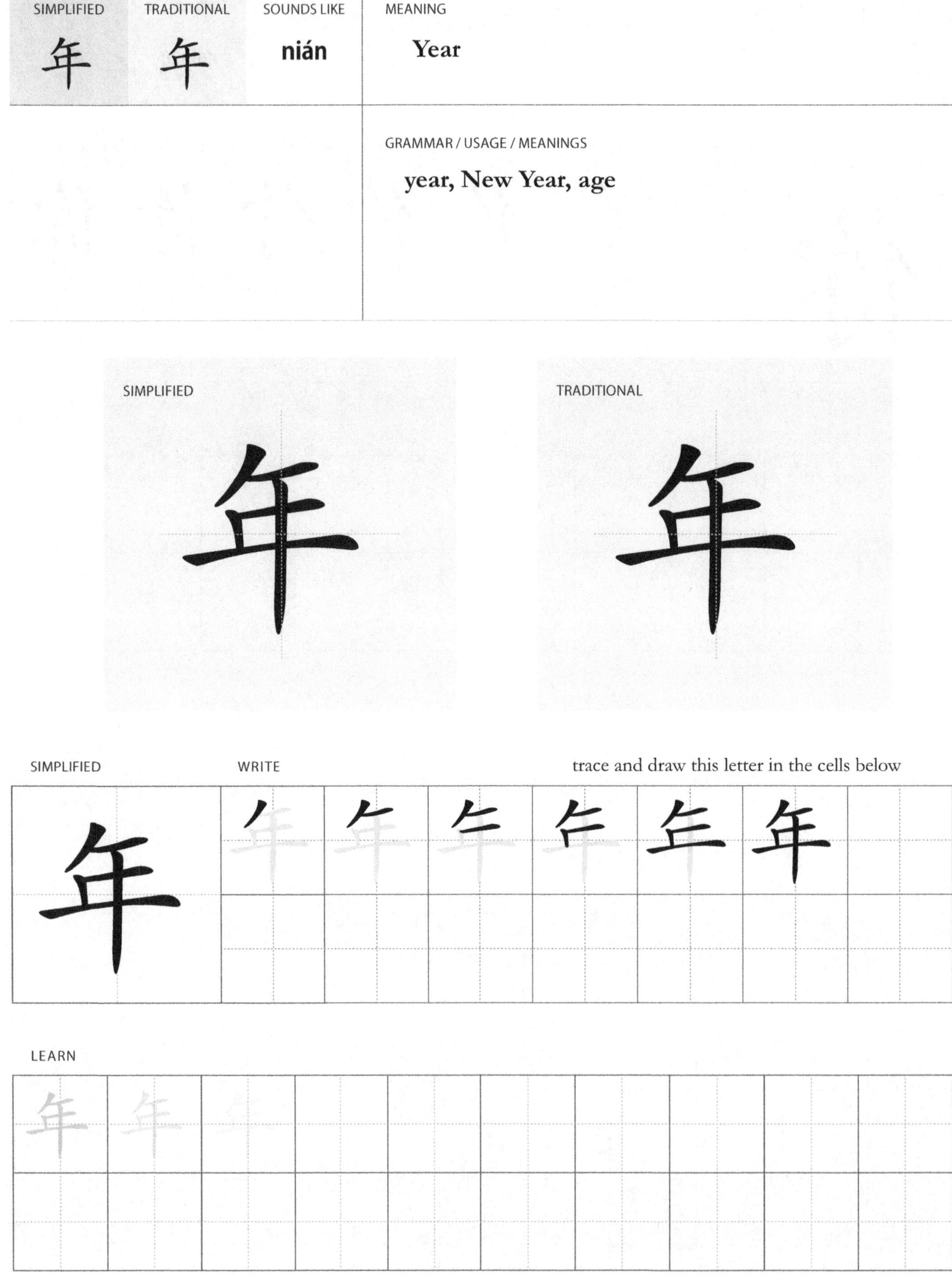

UNICODE SIM. UNICODE TRAD.

24180 **24180**

TRADITIONAL

年

WRITE

trace and draw this letter in the cells below

LEARN

PRACTICE

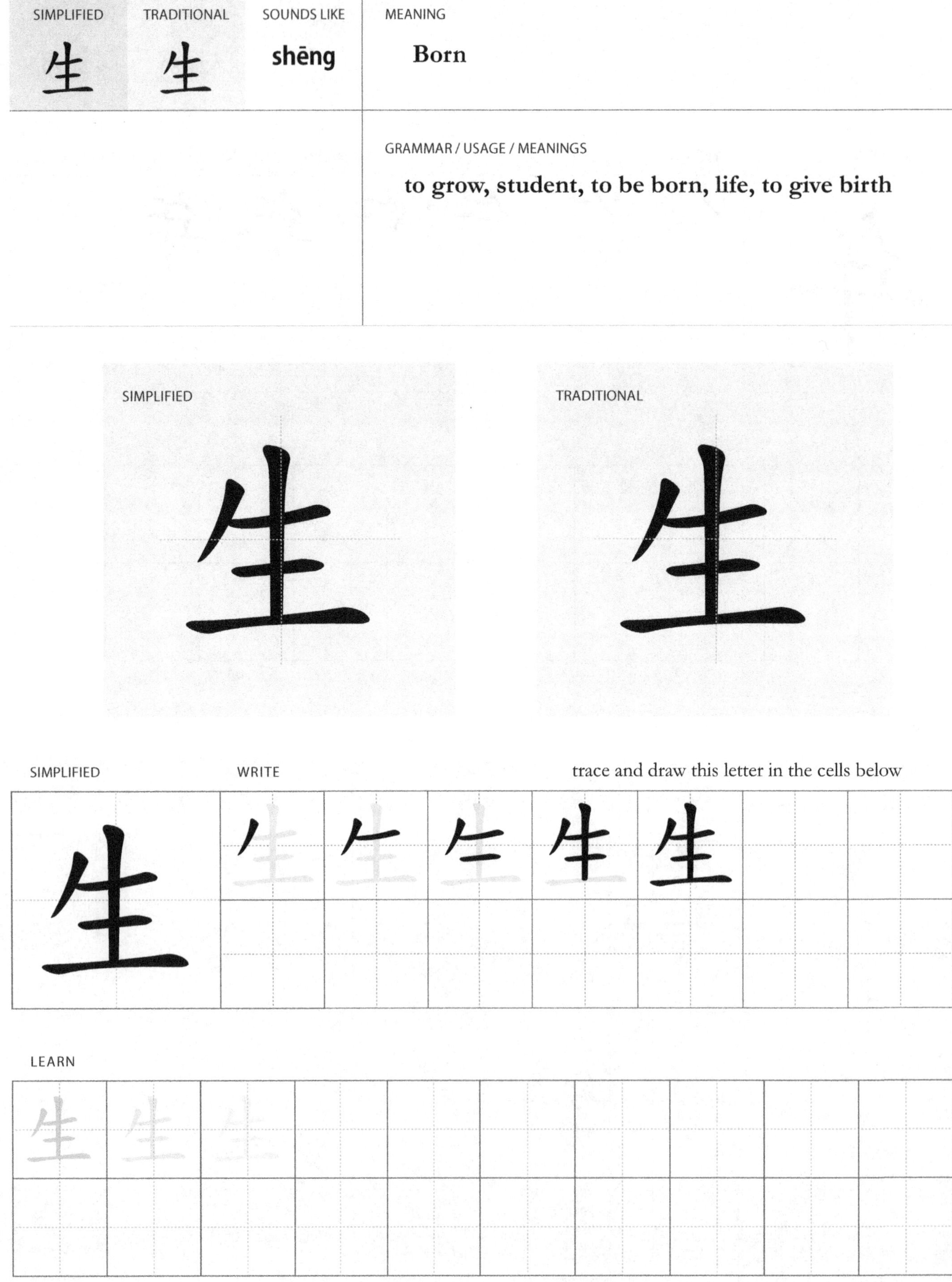
SIMPLIFIED
生
TRADITIONAL
生
SOUNDS LIKE
shēng
MEANING
Born
GRAMMAR / USAGE / MEANINGS
to grow, student, to be born, life, to give birth
SIMPLIFIED
生
TRADITIONAL
生
SIMPLIFIED
WRITE
trace and draw this letter in the cells below
生
LEARN

UNICODE SIM.	UNICODE TRAD.
29983	29983

TRADITIONAL

生

WRITE

trace and draw this letter in the cells below

丿 𠂉 𠂉 牛 生

LEARN

生 生 生

PRACTICE

SIMPLIFIED	TRADITIONAL	SOUNDS LIKE	MEANING
自	自	zì	**Since**

GRAMMAR / USAGE / MEANINGS

oneself, since, from, self

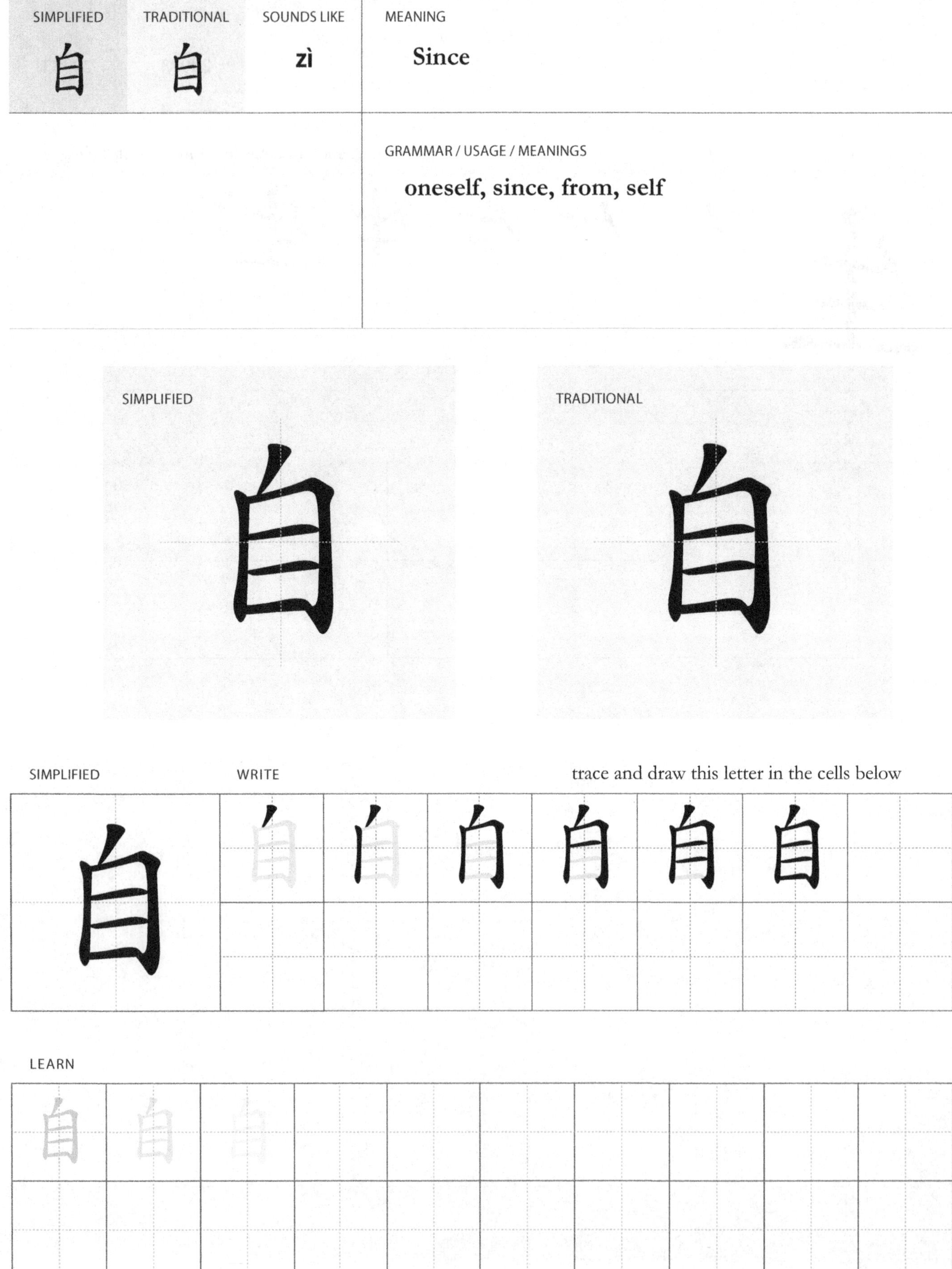

UNICODE SIM.	UNICODE TRAD.
33258	33258

TRADITIONAL

自

WRITE

trace and draw this letter in the cells below

LEARN

PRACTICE

SIMPLIFIED	TRADITIONAL	SOUNDS LIKE	MEANING
会	會	**huì**	**Meeting**

GRAMMAR / USAGE / MEANINGS

society, meeting, union, party, can, meet, able

SIMPLIFIED

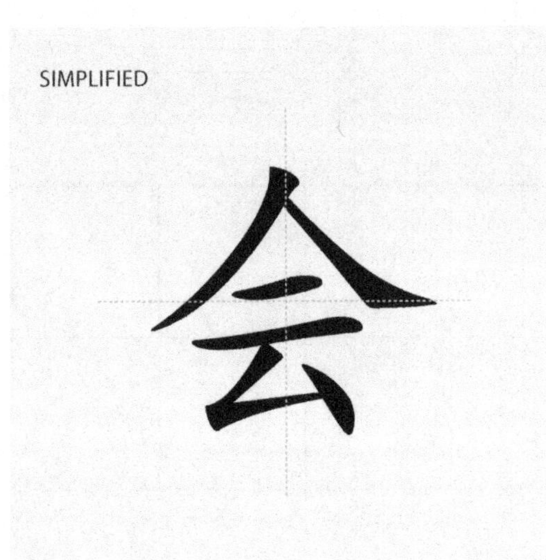

TRADITIONAL

SIMPLIFIED WRITE trace and draw this letter in the cells below

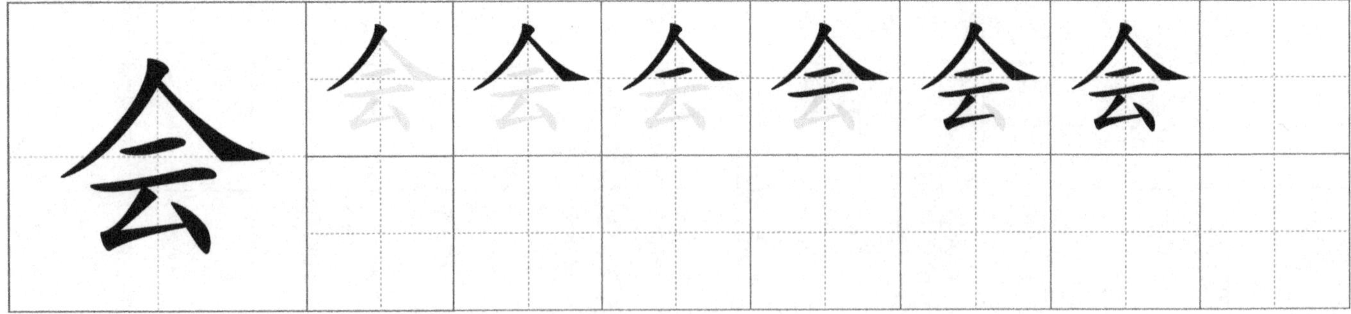

LEARN

UNICODE SIM.	UNICODE TRAD.
20250	**26371**

TRADITIONAL

會

WRITE

trace and draw this letter in the cells below

LEARN

PRACTICE

SIMPLIFIED	TRADITIONAL	SOUNDS LIKE	MEANING
那	那	nà	That

GRAMMAR / USAGE / MEANINGS

that, those

SIMPLIFIED

那

TRADITIONAL

那

SIMPLIFIED

那

WRITE

trace and draw this letter in the cells below

那 那 那 那 那 那

LEARN

那 那 那

UNICODE SIM.	UNICODE TRAD.
37027	**37027**

TRADITIONAL

那

WRITE

trace and draw this letter in the cells below

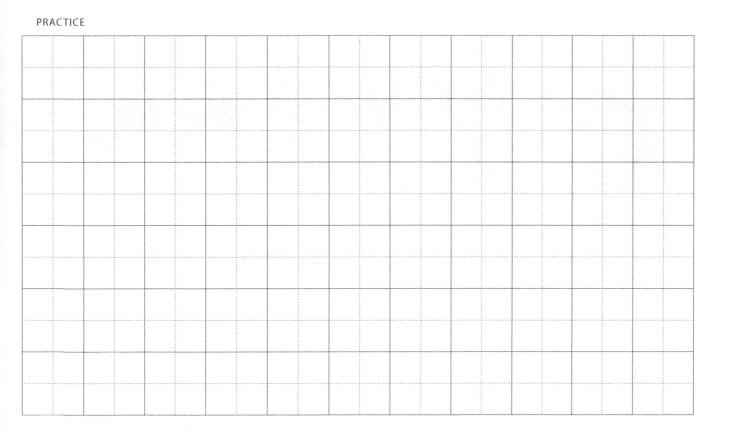

LEARN

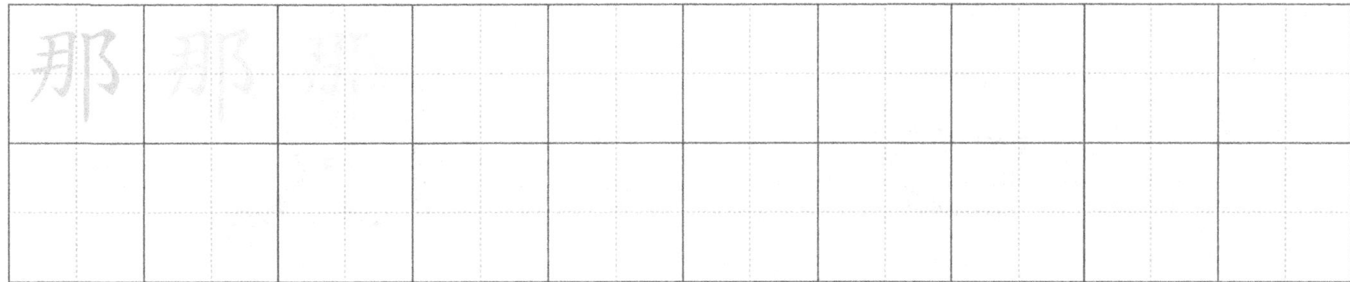

PRACTICE

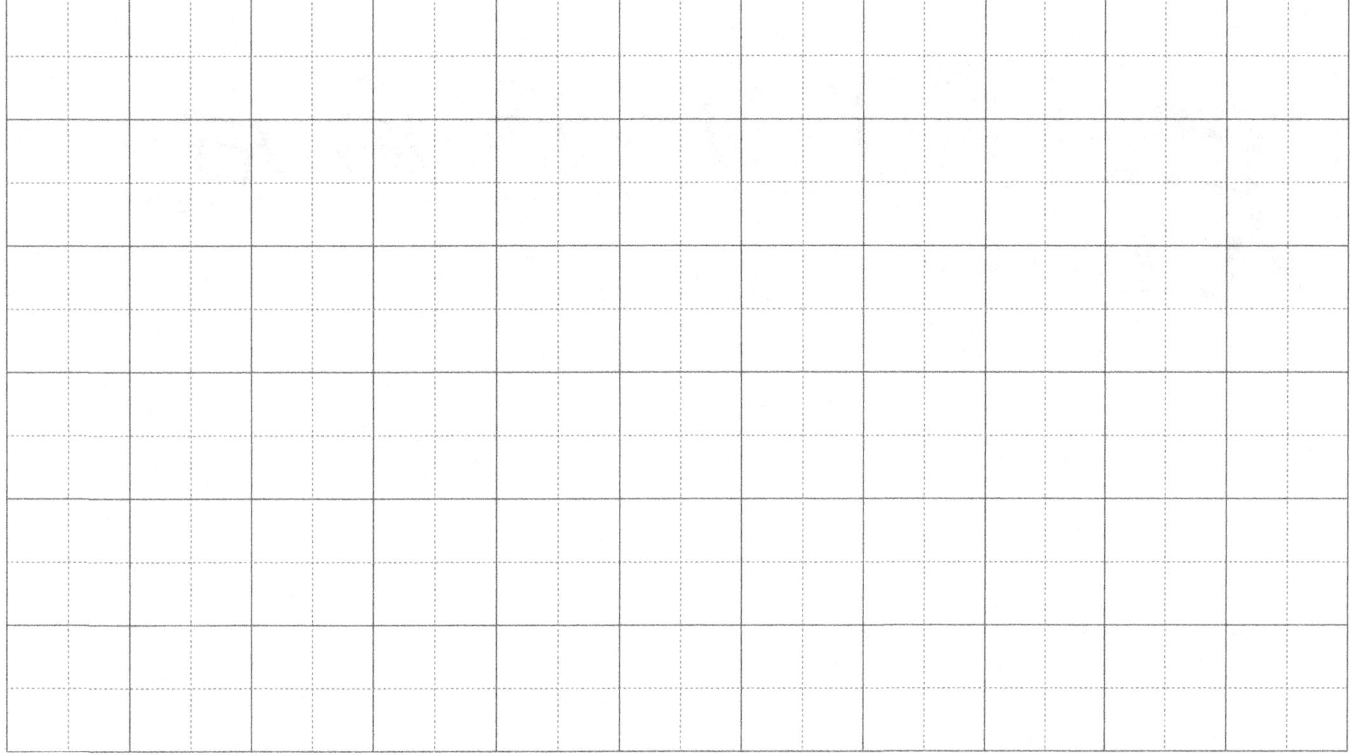

SIMPLIFIED	TRADITIONAL	SOUNDS LIKE	MEANING
后	後	**hòu**	**After**

GRAMMAR / USAGE / MEANINGS

back, later, behind, after, rear, back, last, afterwards, empress

SIMPLIFIED

后

TRADITIONAL

後

SIMPLIFIED

WRITE

trace and draw this letter in the cells below

后

后后后后后后

LEARN

后后后

UNICODE SIM.	UNICODE TRAD.
21518	24460

TRADITIONAL

後

WRITE

trace and draw this letter in the cells below

LEARN

PRACTICE

SIMPLIFIED	TRADITIONAL	SOUNDS LIKE	MEANING
能	能	**néng**	**Can**

GRAMMAR / USAGE / MEANINGS

can, may, ability, skill, capable, able, energy

SIMPLIFIED

能

TRADITIONAL

能

SIMPLIFIED WRITE trace and draw this letter in the cells below

LEARN

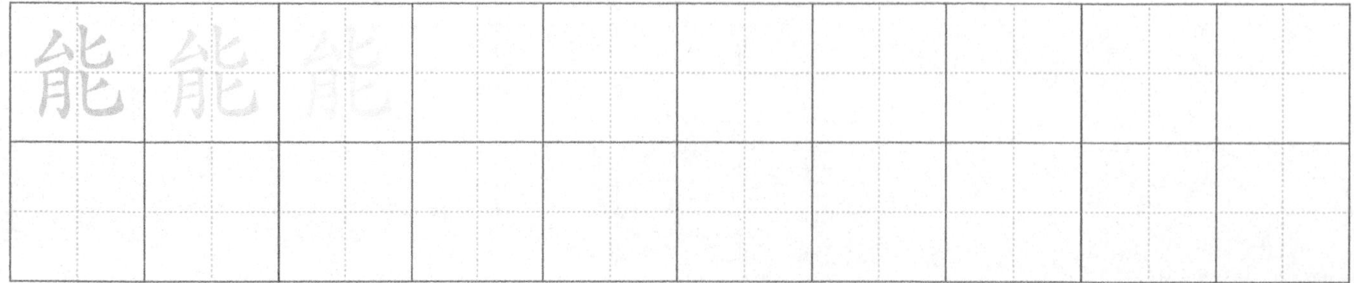

UNICODE SIM.	UNICODE TRAD.
33021	33021

TRADITIONAL WRITE trace and draw this letter in the cells below

能

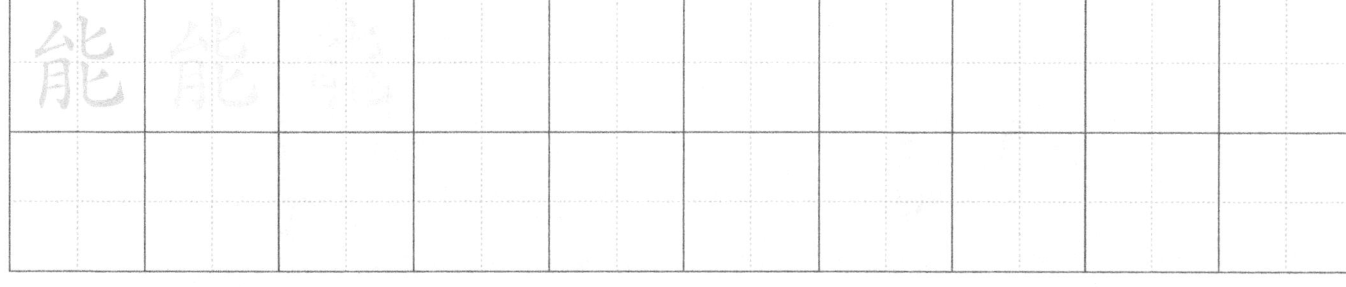

LEARN

PRACTICE

SIMPLIFIED	TRADITIONAL	SOUNDS LIKE	MEANING
对	對	**duì**	**Right**

GRAMMAR / USAGE / MEANINGS

correct (answer), to answer, to reply, to direct (towards something), right, pair, couple, to be opposite, for, to, to oppose, to face

TRADITIONAL

對

SIMPLIFIED WRITE trace and draw this letter in the cells below

LEARN

UNICODE SIM.	UNICODE TRAD.
23545	23565

TRADITIONAL

對

WRITE

trace and draw this letter in the cells below

LEARN

PRACTICE

SIMPLIFIED	TRADITIONAL	SOUNDS LIKE	MEANING
着	著	**zhe/zhuó/ zhāo/zháo**	Write

GRAMMAR / USAGE / MEANINGS

verb particle marking a continuing progress /state

SIMPLIFIED 着

TRADITIONAL 著

SIMPLIFIED

WRITE

trace and draw this letter in the cells below

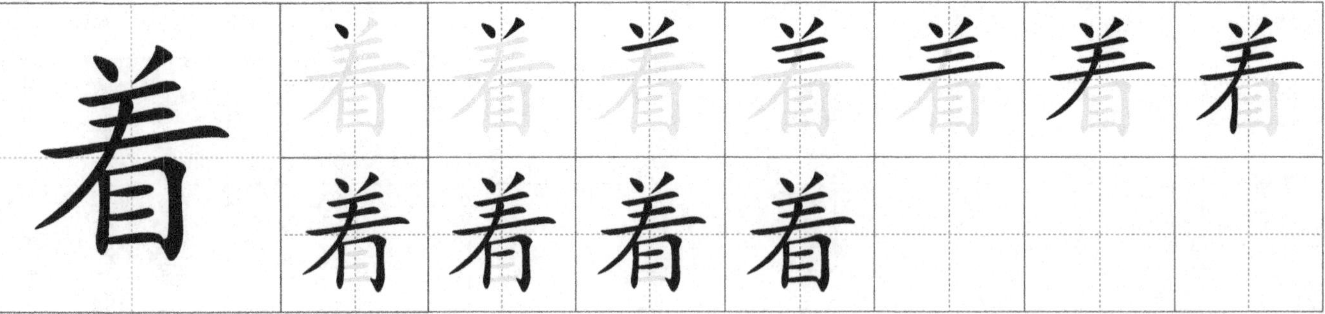

LEARN

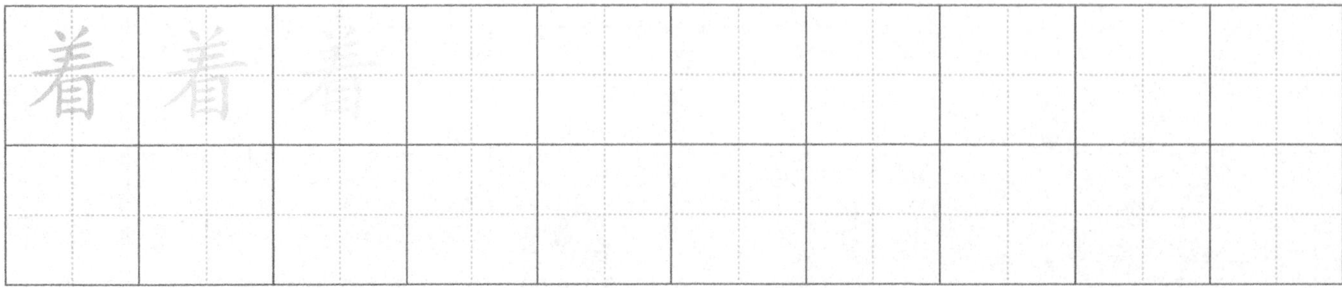

UNICODE SIM.	UNICODE TRAD.
30528	33879

TRADITIONAL

著

WRITE

trace and draw this letter in the cells below

著 著 著 著

LEARN

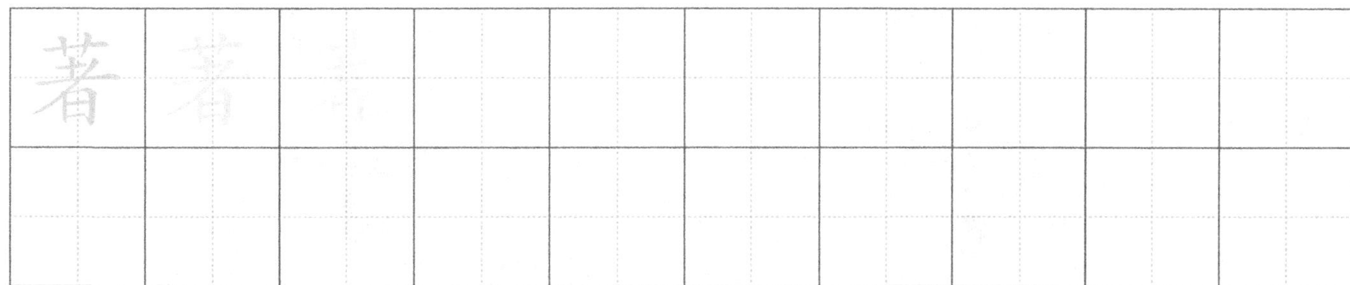

PRACTICE

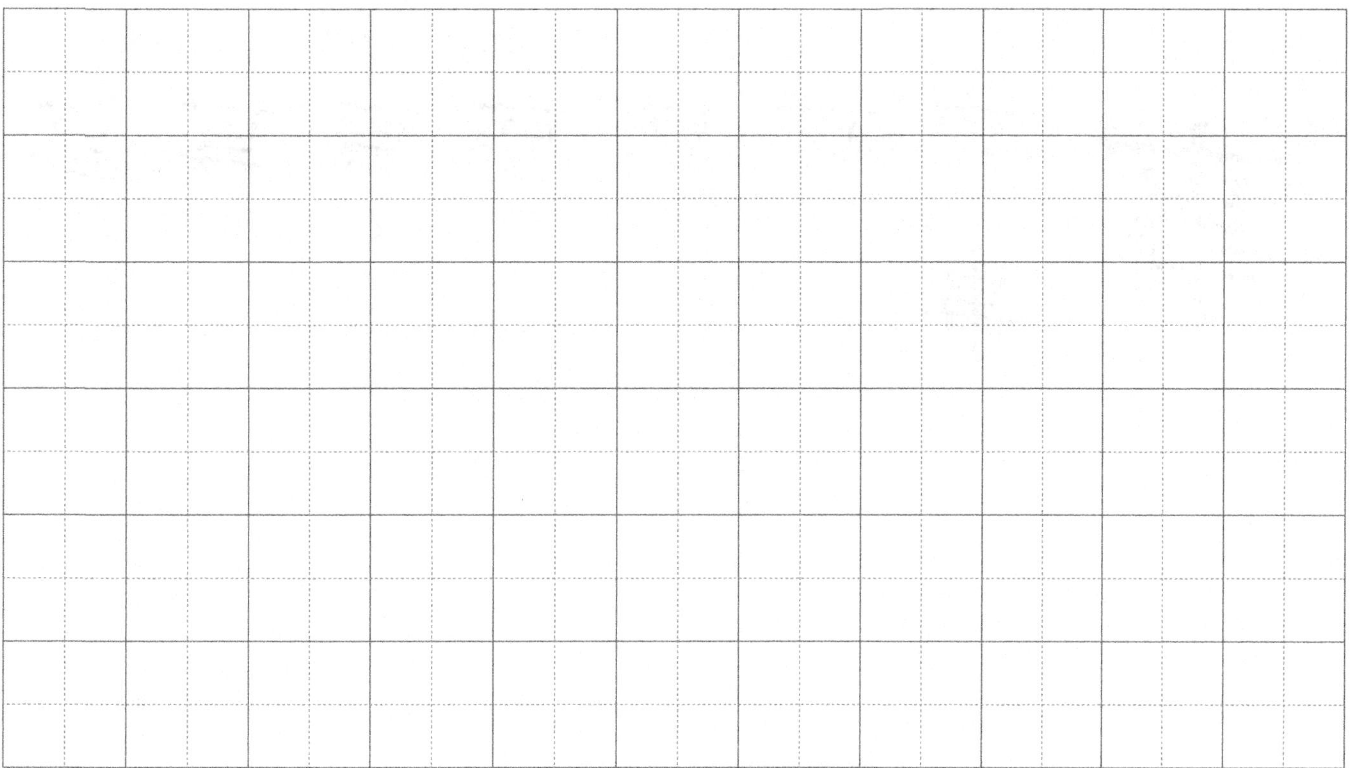

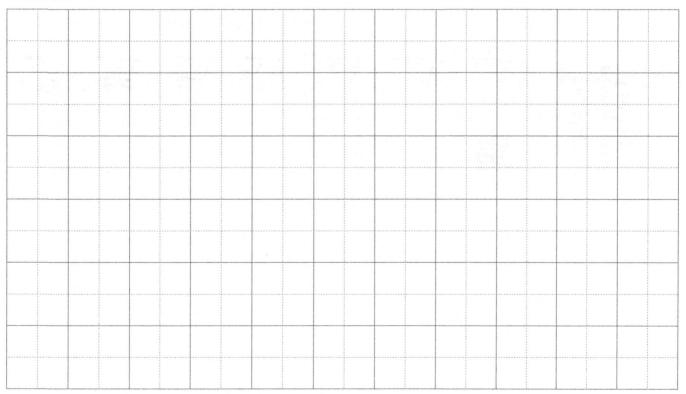

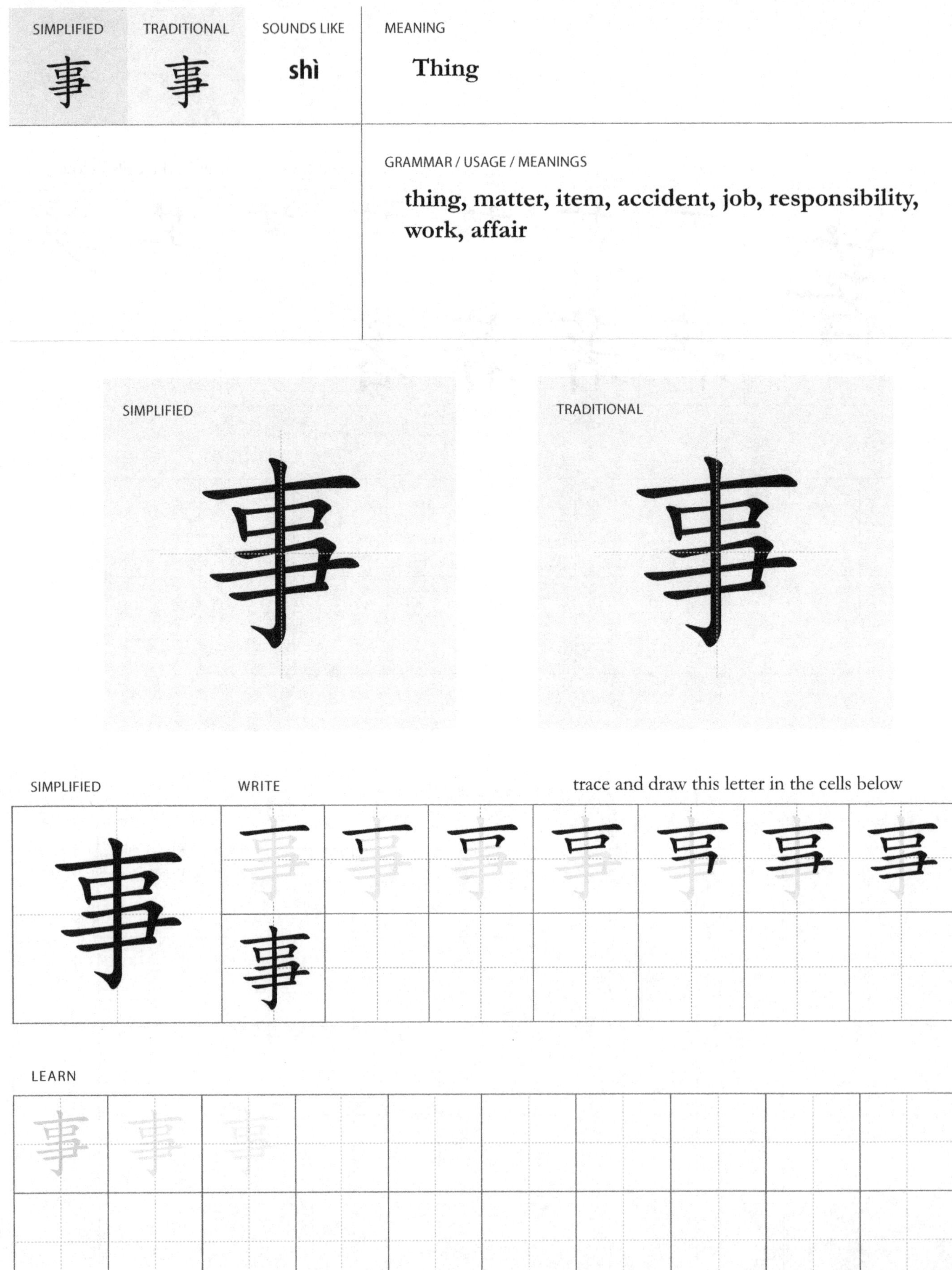
SIMPLIFIED
事
TRADITIONAL
事
SOUNDS LIKE
shì
MEANING
Thing
GRAMMAR / USAGE / MEANINGS
thing, matter, item, accident, job, responsibility, work, affair
SIMPLIFIED
事
TRADITIONAL
事
SIMPLIFIED
事
WRITE
trace and draw this letter in the cells below
事
LEARN

UNICODE SIM.	UNICODE TRAD.
20107	20107

TRADITIONAL

事

WRITE

trace and draw this letter in the cells below

一 丅 亖 亖 亖 亖 亖 事

LEARN

事 事

PRACTICE

SIMPLIFIED	TRADITIONAL	SOUNDS LIKE	MEANING
其	其	qí	Its

GRAMMAR / USAGE / MEANINGS

his, her, its, theirs, that, such, it (refers to something preceding it)

TRADITIONAL

其

SIMPLIFIED　　WRITE　　trace and draw this letter in the cells below

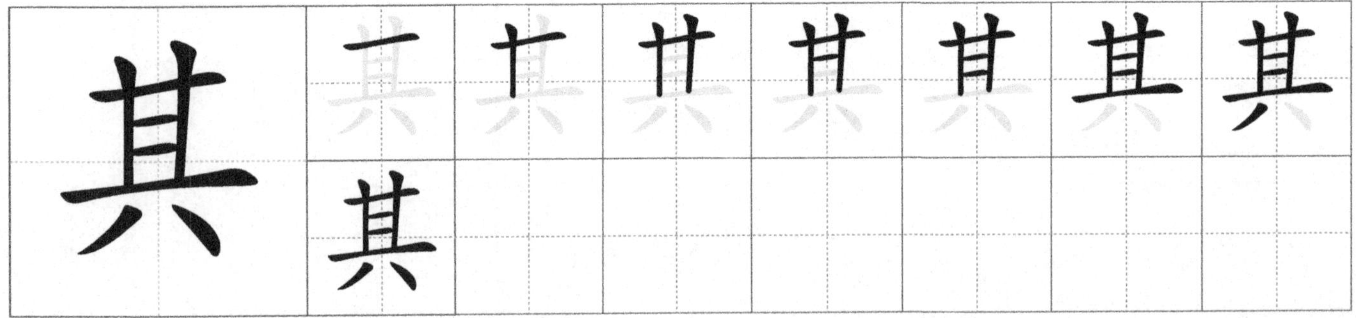

LEARN

UNICODE SIM.	UNICODE TRAD.
20854	**20854**

TRADITIONAL

其

WRITE

trace and draw this letter in the cells below

一 十 廾 甘 甘 甚 其 其

LEARN

其 其

PRACTICE

SIMPLIFIED	TRADITIONAL	SOUNDS LIKE	MEANING
里	裏 OR 裡	lǐ	Inside

GRAMMAR / USAGE / MEANINGS

within, inside, neighbourhood, hometown, inner, a Chinese unit of length (= 1/2 kilometre)

SIMPLIFIED

里

TRADITIONAL

裏 OR 裡

SIMPLIFIED

WRITE

trace and draw this letter in the cells below

里

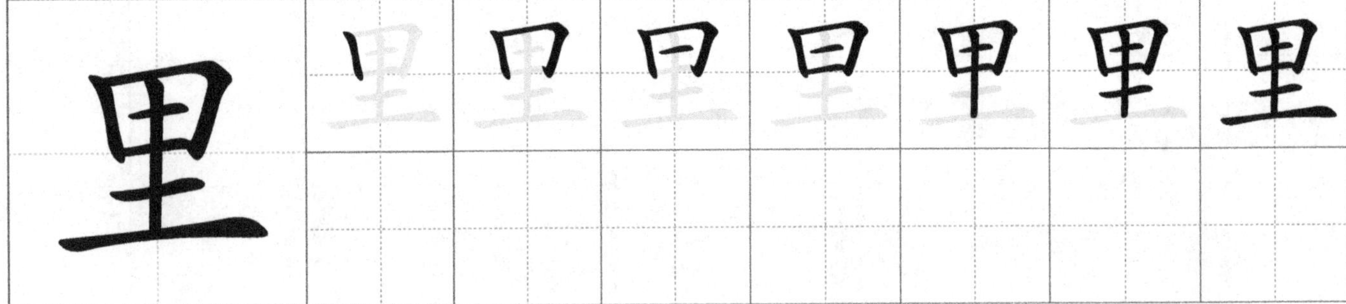

LEARN

UNICODE SIM.	UNICODE TRAD.
37324	35023 or 35041

TRADITIONAL　WRITE　trace and draw this letter in the cells below

裏

裡

LEARN

PRACTICE

SIMPLIFIED	TRADITIONAL	SOUNDS LIKE	MEANING
所	所	**suǒ**	**Place**

GRAMMAR / USAGE / MEANINGS

actually, place

SIMPLIFIED

所

TRADITIONAL

所

SIMPLIFIED

WRITE

trace and draw this letter in the cells below

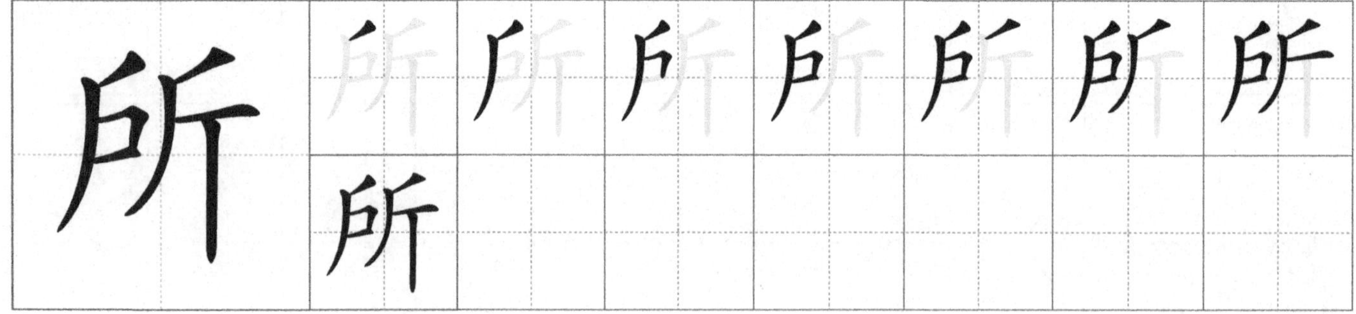

LEARN

所 所 所

UNICODE SIM.	UNICODE TRAD.
25152	**25152**

TRADITIONAL

WRITE

trace and draw this letter in the cells below

所

LEARN

PRACTICE

SIMPLIFIED	TRADITIONAL	SOUNDS LIKE	MEANING
去	去	**qù**	**Go**

GRAMMAR / USAGE / MEANINGS

to leave, to go, to send, be apart from, to depart, to remove

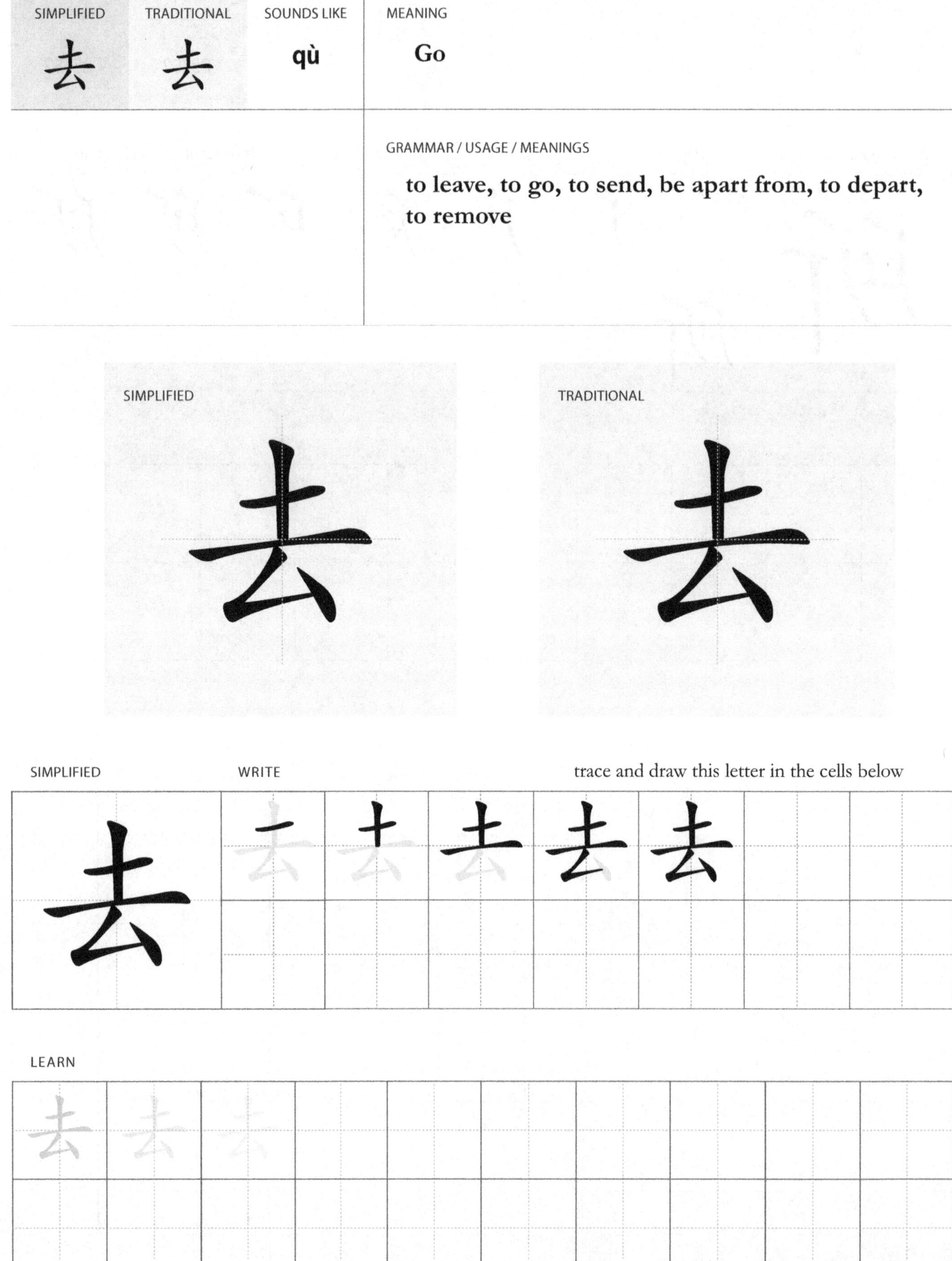

UNICODE SIM.	UNICODE TRAD.
21435	**21435**

TRADITIONAL

去

WRITE

trace and draw this letter in the cells below

一 十 土 去 去

LEARN

去 去

PRACTICE

SIMPLIFIED	TRADITIONAL	SOUNDS LIKE	MEANING
行	行	**háng/xíng**	Line

GRAMMAR / USAGE / MEANINGS

a row, profession, to go, professional / all right, will do / behavior, conduct, capable, competent, okay, to do, to travel, temporary, to walk

TRADITIONAL

行

SIMPLIFIED WRITE trace and draw this letter in the cells below

LEARN

UNICODE SIM.	UNICODE TRAD.
34892	**34892**

TRADITIONAL

行

WRITE

trace and draw this letter in the cells below

LEARN

PRACTICE

SIMPLIFIED	TRADITIONAL	SOUNDS LIKE	MEANING
过	過	guò	**Over**

GRAMMAR / USAGE / MEANINGS

(past tense marker), undue, exceed, excessive, (surname), to cross, to go over, across, through, over, to pass (time), to live, to get along, after, past

SIMPLIFIED

TRADITIONAL

过 過

SIMPLIFIED WRITE trace and draw this letter in the cells below

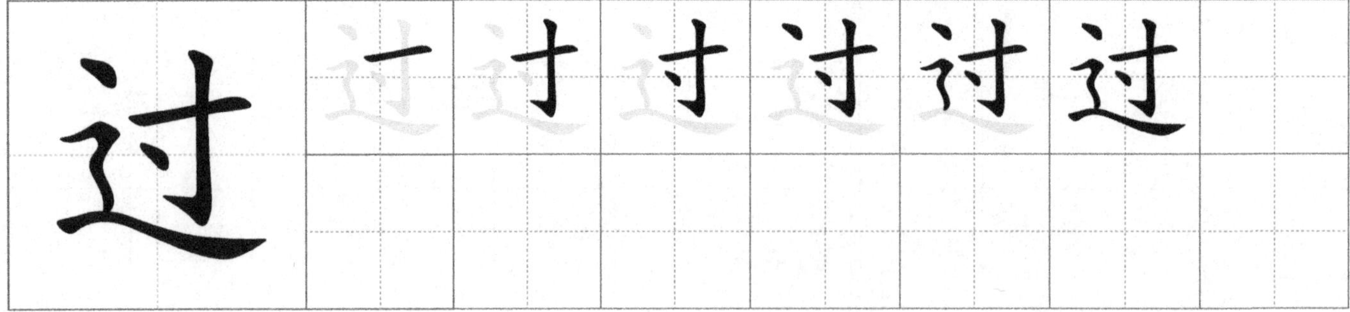

LEARN

UNICODE SIM.	UNICODE TRAD.
36807	**36942**

TRADITIONAL

過

WRITE

trace and draw this letter in the cells below

LEARN

過 過

PRACTICE

SIMPLIFIED	TRADITIONAL	SOUNDS LIKE	MEANING
家	家	**jiā**	**Home**

GRAMMAR / USAGE / MEANINGS

home, family, a school of thought, a person engaged in a certain art or profession

TRADITIONAL

家

SIMPLIFIED WRITE trace and draw this letter in the cells below

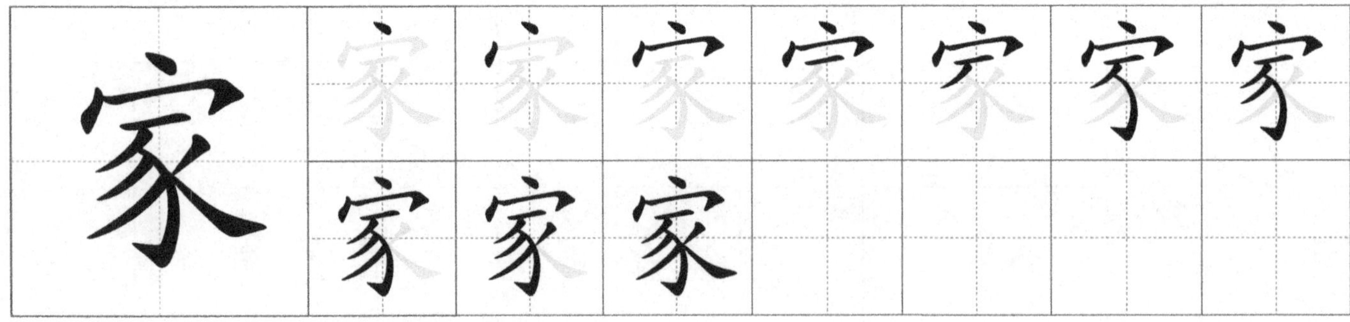

LEARN

UNICODE SIM.	UNICODE TRAD.
23478	23478

TRADITIONAL

家

WRITE

trace and draw this letter in the cells below

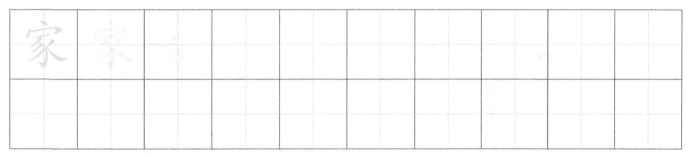

LEARN

家 家 家

PRACTICE

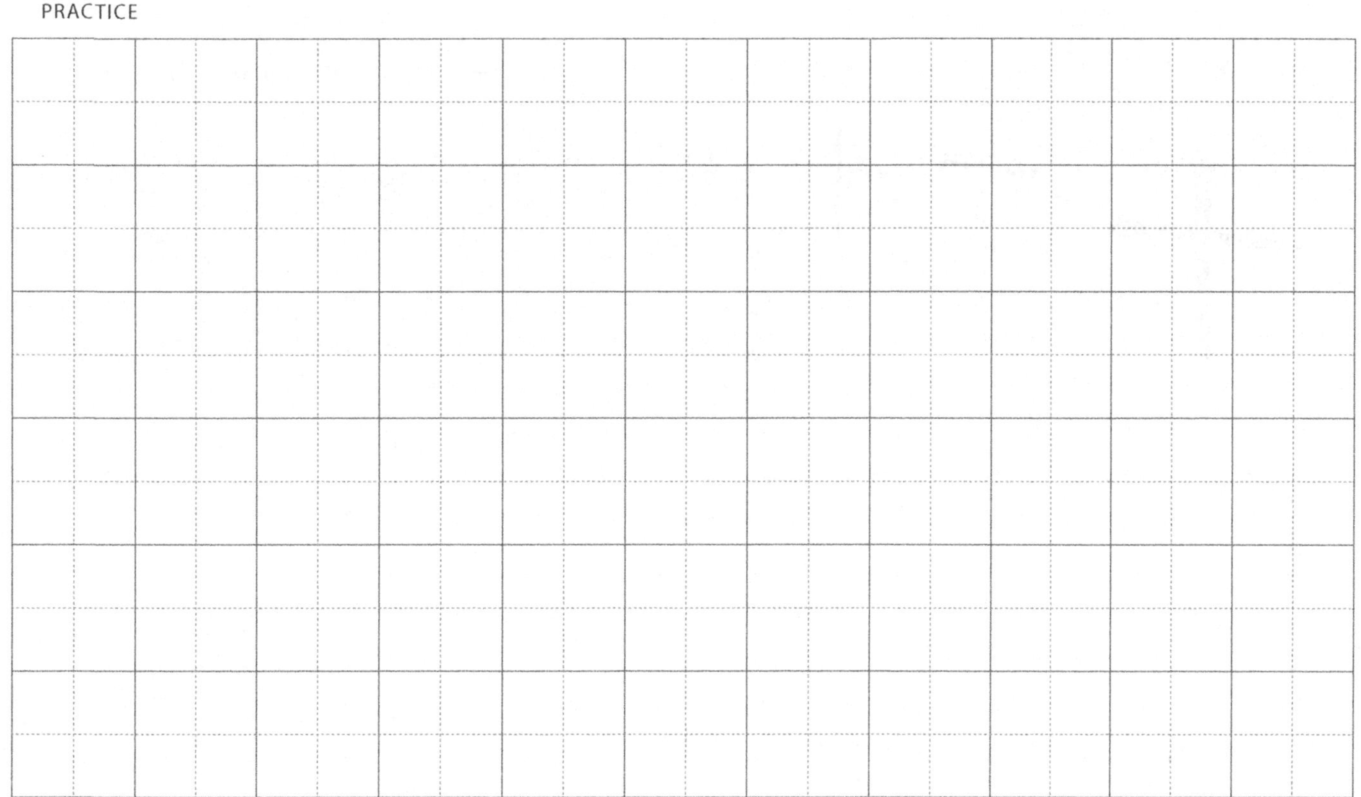

SIMPLIFIED	TRADITIONAL	SOUNDS LIKE	MEANING
十	十	**shí**	**Ten**

GRAMMAR / USAGE / MEANINGS

ten, topmost

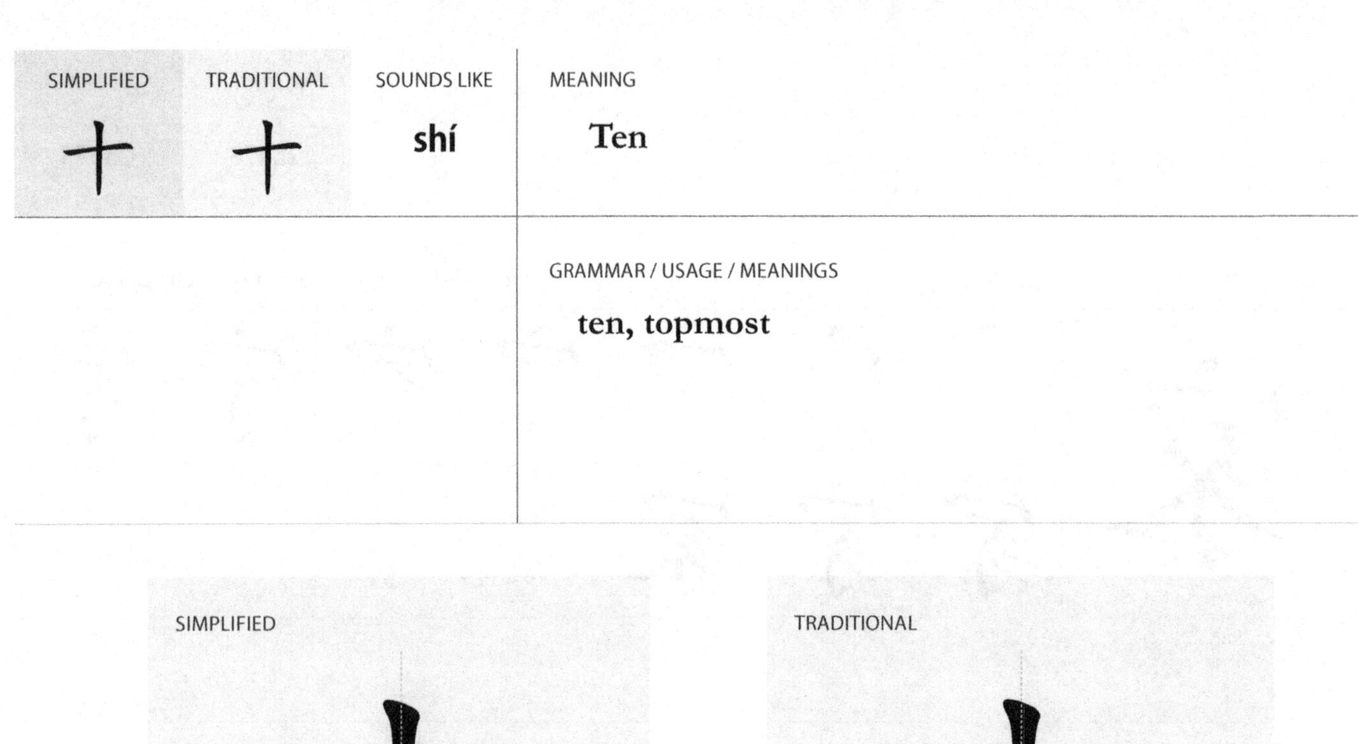

SIMPLIFIED

十

TRADITIONAL

十

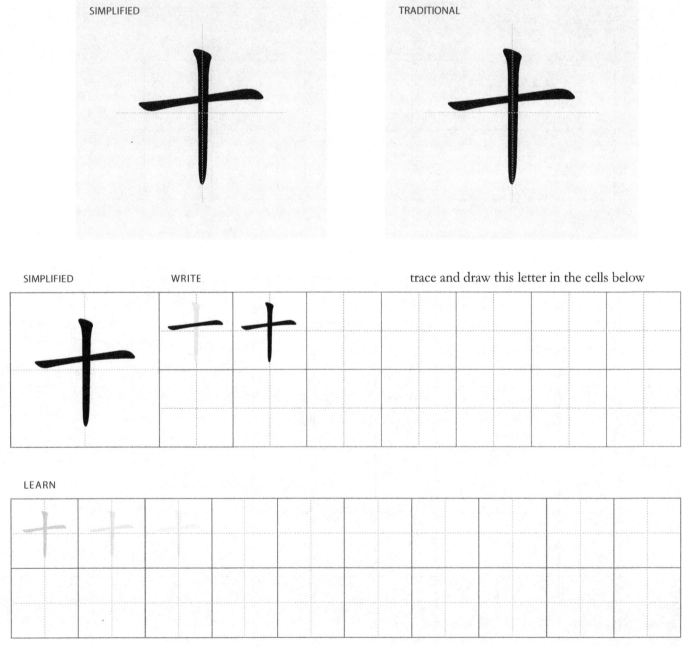

SIMPLIFIED

十

WRITE

trace and draw this letter in the cells below

LEARN

UNICODE SIM.	UNICODE TRAD.
21313	21313

TRADITIONAL

十

WRITE

一 十

trace and draw this letter in the cells below

LEARN

PRACTICE

SIMPLIFIED	TRADITIONAL	SOUNDS LIKE	MEANING
用	用	yòng	Use

GRAMMAR / USAGE / MEANINGS

to use, need, to eat, to drink

SIMPLIFIED

用

TRADITIONAL

用

SIMPLIFIED　WRITE　trace and draw this letter in the cells below

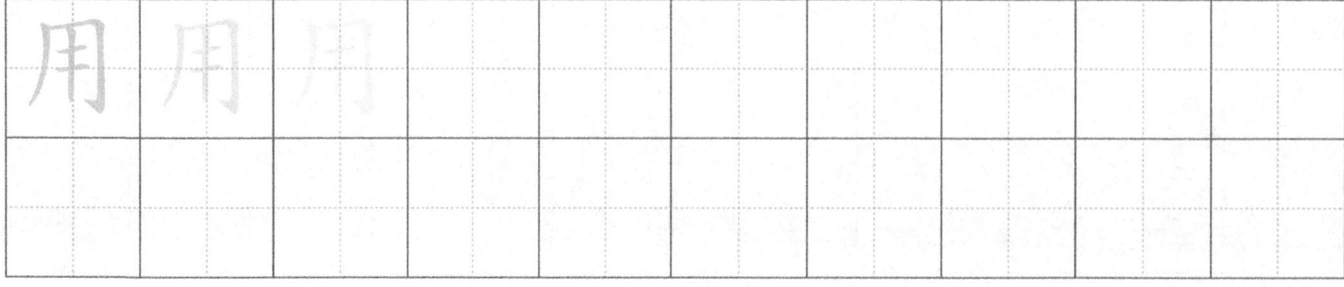

LEARN

UNICODE SIM.	UNICODE TRAD.
29992	29992

TRADITIONAL

用

WRITE

trace and draw this letter in the cells below

LEARN

PRACTICE

SIMPLIFIED

发

TRADITIONAL

發 OR 髮

SOUNDS LIKE

fā / fà

MEANING

SIM=hair,
TRAD 發=to send ; 髮=hair

GRAMMAR / USAGE / MEANINGS

to send out, to show (one‘s feeling), flourish, to spread out, to expose, to issue,, to become, to develop / hair, to launch, to produce, to express

SIMPLIFIED

发

TRADITIONAL

OR 髮

SIMPLIFIED

WRITE

trace and draw this letter in the cells below

发

LEARN

发 发 发

UNICODE SIM.	UNICODE TRAD.
21457	30332 or 39662

TRADITIONAL

發

髮

WRITE

trace and draw this letter in the cells below

LEARN

PRACTICE

SIMPLIFIED	TRADITIONAL	SOUNDS LIKE	MEANING
天	天	tiān	Sky

GRAMMAR / USAGE / MEANINGS

day, overhead, natural, innate, sky, heaven, a period of time in a day, season, weather, nature

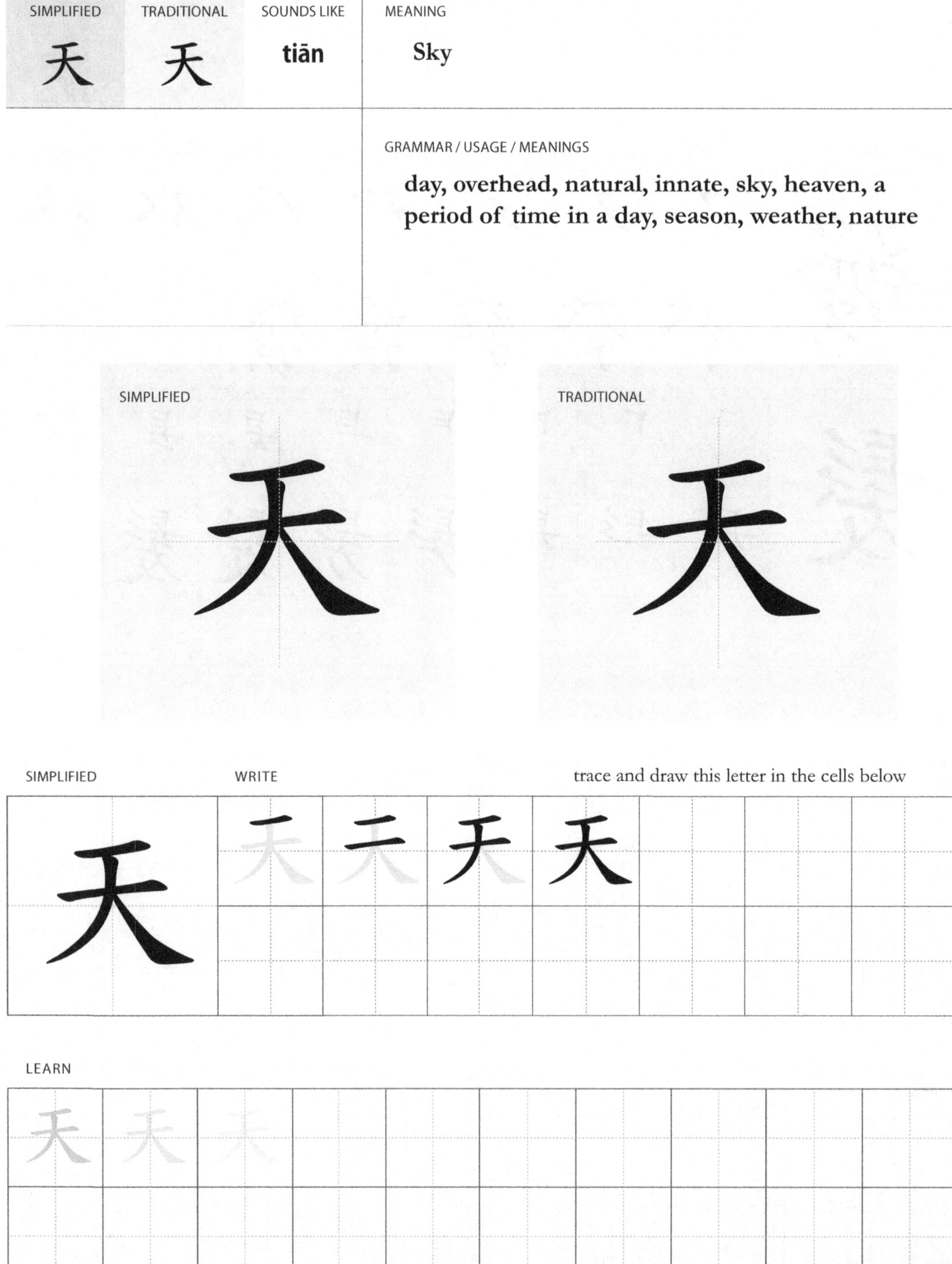

UNICODE SIM.	UNICODE TRAD.
22825	22825

TRADITIONAL

天

WRITE

trace and draw this letter in the cells below

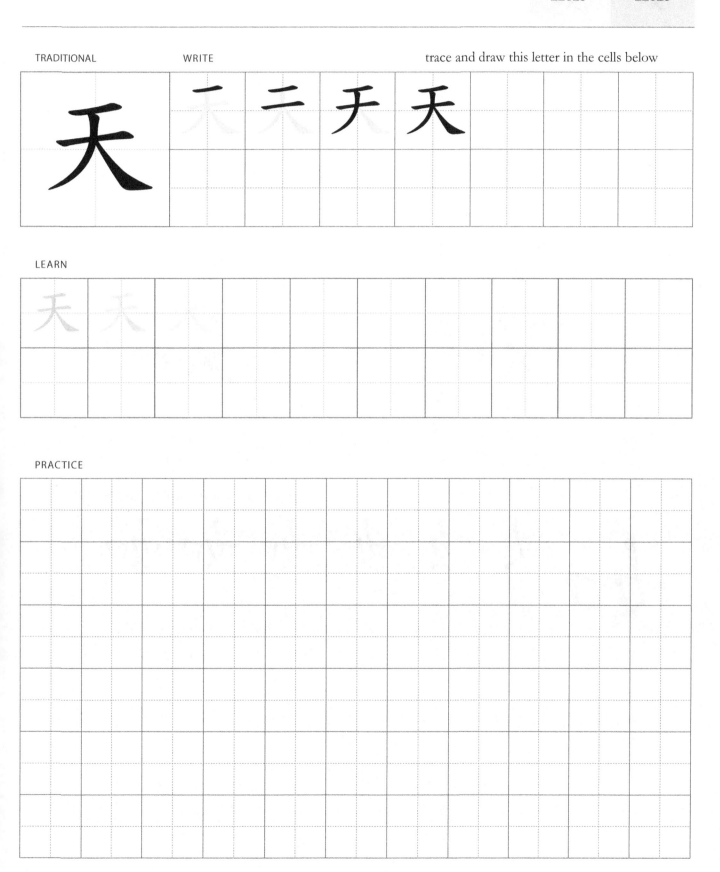

一 二 天 天

LEARN

天 天

PRACTICE

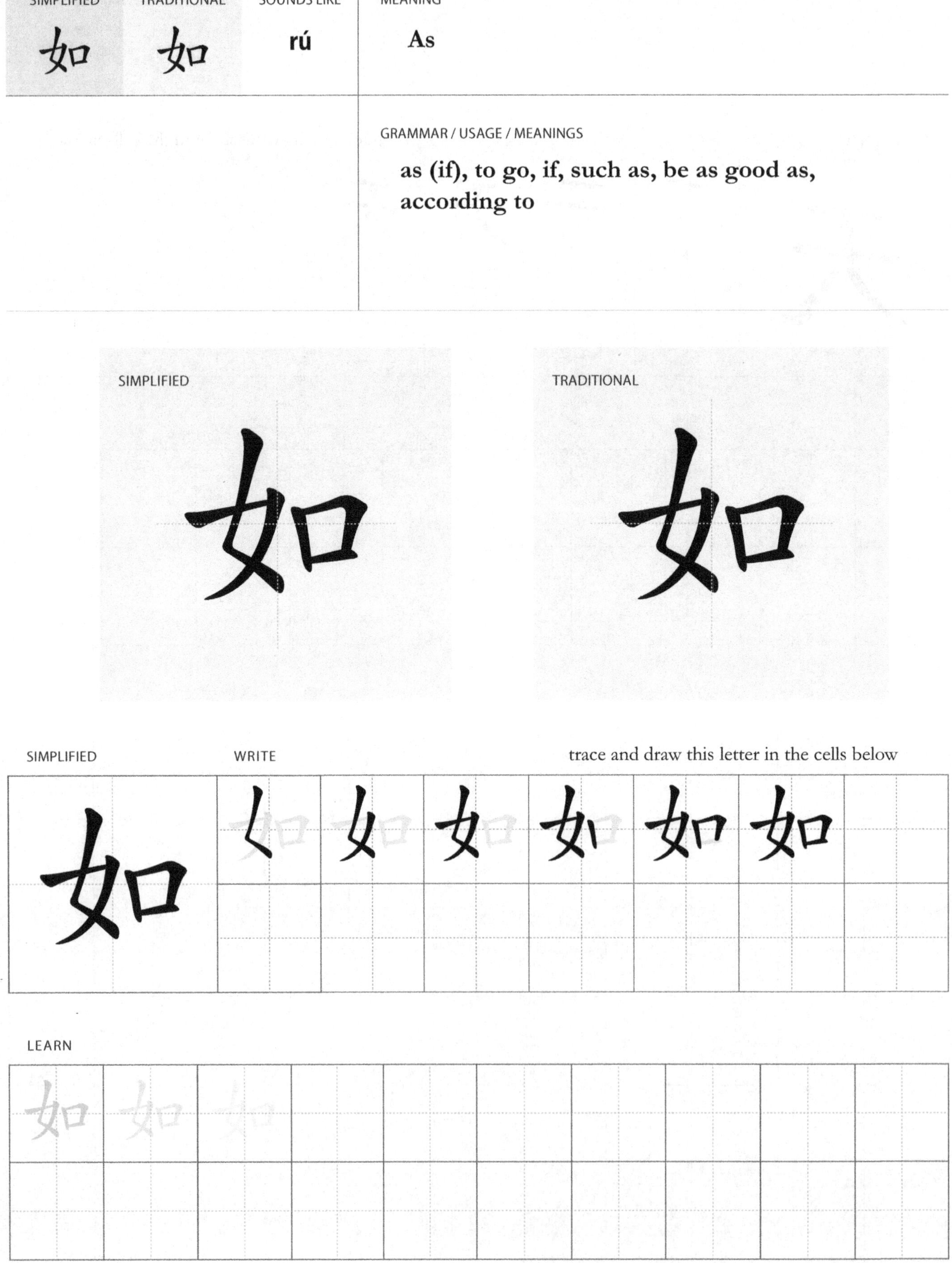

SIMPLIFIED	TRADITIONAL	SOUNDS LIKE	MEANING
如	如	rú	**As**

GRAMMAR / USAGE / MEANINGS

as (if), to go, if, such as, be as good as, according to

SIMPLIFIED

如

TRADITIONAL

如

SIMPLIFIED

如

WRITE

trace and draw this letter in the cells below

LEARN

UNICODE SIM.	UNICODE TRAD.
22914	22914

TRADITIONAL

如

WRITE

trace and draw this letter in the cells below

LEARN

PRACTICE

SIMPLIFIED	TRADITIONAL	SOUNDS LIKE	MEANING
然	然	**rán**	**Yet**

GRAMMAR / USAGE / MEANINGS

correct, right, but, however, thus, so, like this, /ly

SIMPLIFIED

然

TRADITIONAL

然

SIMPLIFIED

WRITE

trace and draw this letter in the cells below

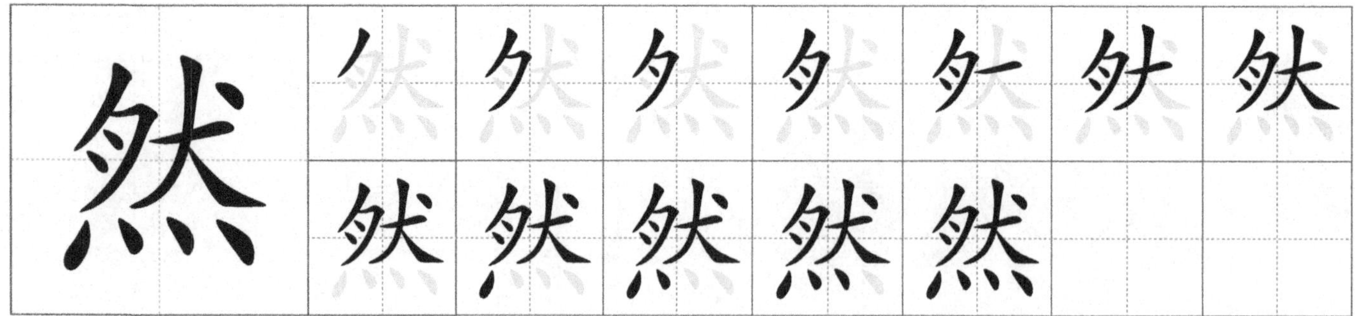

LEARN

UNICODE SIM.	UNICODE TRAD.
28982	28982

TRADITIONAL

然

WRITE

trace and draw this letter in the cells below

LEARN

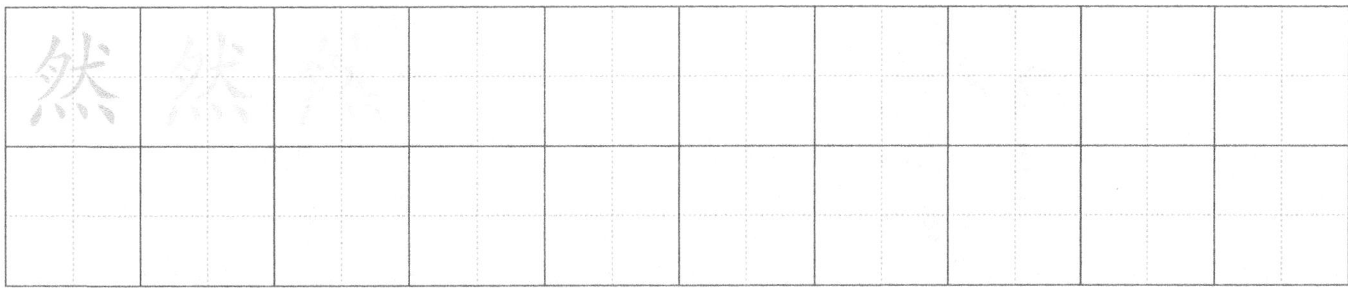

PRACTICE

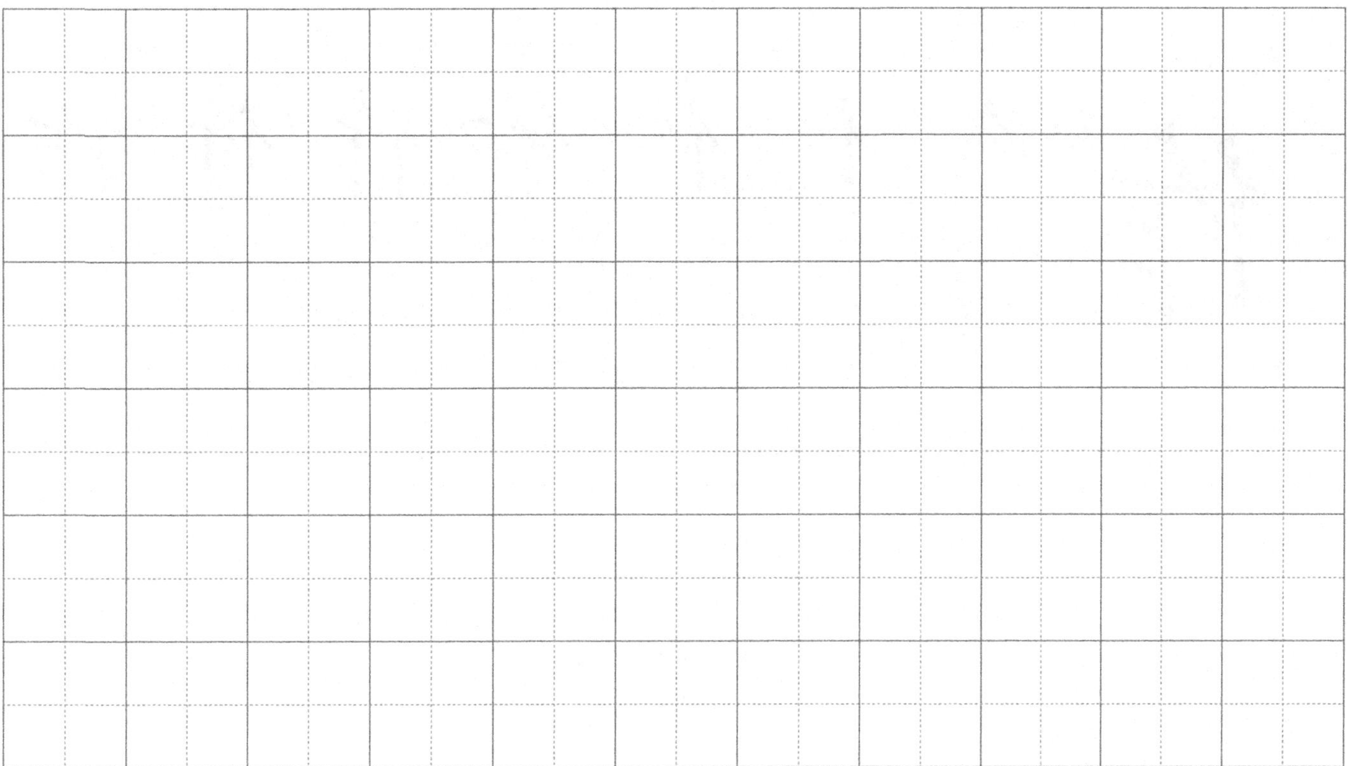

SIMPLIFIED	TRADITIONAL	SOUNDS LIKE	MEANING
作	作	zuò	Do

GRAMMAR / USAGE / MEANINGS

to regard as, to act as, writings, to take (somebody) for, to make, to get up, to write /compose, to pretend, to do

SIMPLIFIED

作

TRADITIONAL

作

SIMPLIFIED

WRITE

trace and draw this letter in the cells below

作

LEARN

UNICODE SIM.	UNICODE TRAD.
20316	20316

TRADITIONAL

作

WRITE

trace and draw this letter in the cells below

LEARN

PRACTICE

SIMPLIFIED	TRADITIONAL	SOUNDS LIKE	MEANING
方	方	**fāng**	**Square**

GRAMMAR / USAGE / MEANINGS

square, power, quadrilateral, prescription, surname, direction, just, side, place, method

SIMPLIFIED

方

TRADITIONAL

方

LEARN

UNICODE SIM.	UNICODE TRAD.
26041	26041

TRADITIONAL

方

WRITE

trace and draw this letter in the cells below

LEARN

PRACTICE

SIMPLIFIED	TRADITIONAL	SOUNDS LIKE	MEANING
成	成	**chéng**	**Become**

GRAMMAR / USAGE / MEANINGS

finish, complete, turn into, succeed, win, accomplish, become

SIMPLIFIED

成

TRADITIONAL

成

SIMPLIFIED

WRITE

trace and draw this letter in the cells below

成

LEARN

UNICODE SIM.	UNICODE TRAD.
25104	25104

TRADITIONAL

成

WRITE

trace and draw this letter in the cells below

一 厂 万 成 成 成

LEARN

成 成 成

PRACTICE

SIMPLIFIED	TRADITIONAL	SOUNDS LIKE	MEANING
者	者	**zhě**	**The**

GRAMMAR / USAGE / MEANINGS

person (who does something), /ist, /er (person)

SIMPLIFIED

者

TRADITIONAL

者

SIMPLIFIED

者

WRITE

trace and draw this letter in the cells below

者 者 者 者 者 者 者 者

LEARN

者 者 者

UNICODE SIM.	UNICODE TRAD.
32773	32773

TRADITIONAL

者

WRITE

trace and draw this letter in the cells below

一 十 土 耂 者 者 者 者

LEARN

者 者 者

PRACTICE

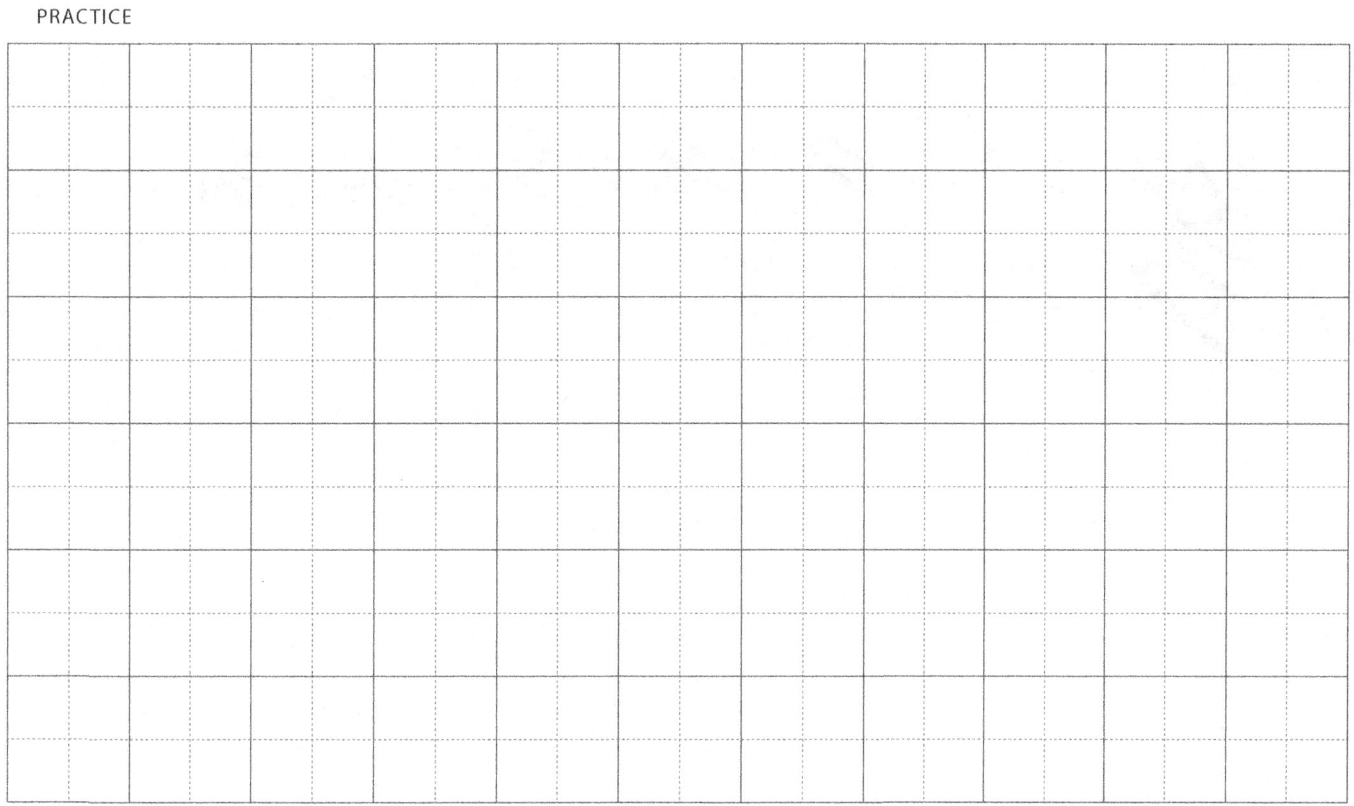

SIMPLIFIED	TRADITIONAL	SOUNDS LIKE	MEANING
多	多	duō	More

GRAMMAR / USAGE / MEANINGS

many, much, too many, too much, more, exceed a number, a lot of, numerous, multi/

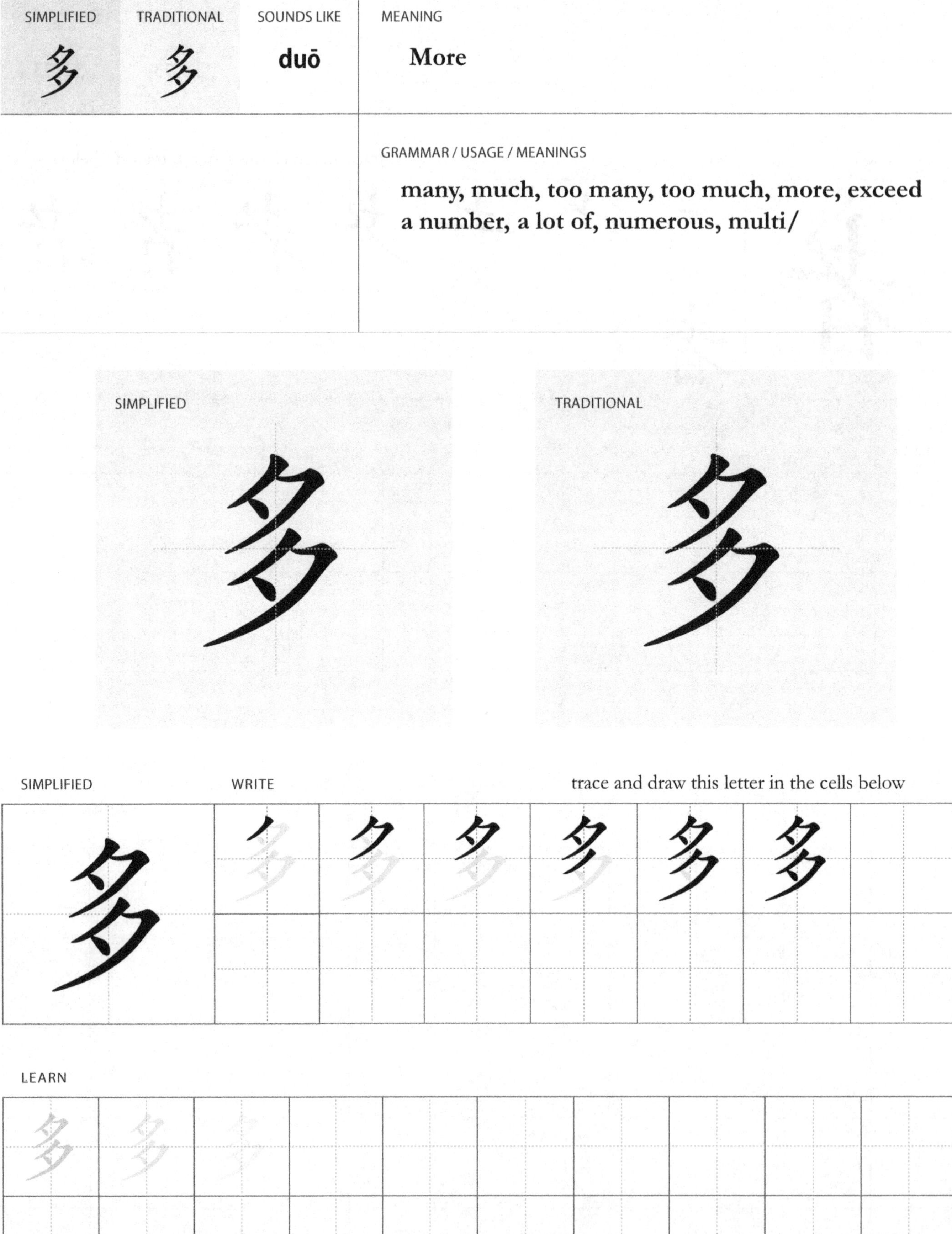

UNICODE SIM.	UNICODE TRAD.
22810	22810

TRADITIONAL

多

WRITE

trace and draw this letter in the cells below

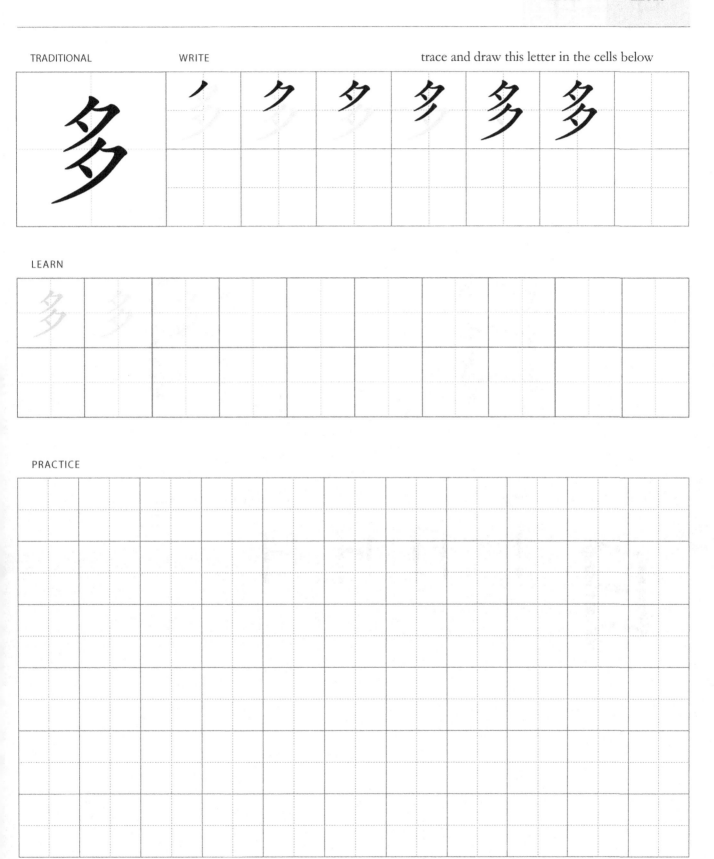

丿 夕 夕 多 多 多

LEARN

多 多

PRACTICE

SIMPLIFIED	TRADITIONAL	SOUNDS LIKE	MEANING
日	日	rì	**Day**

GRAMMAR / USAGE / MEANINGS

day, sun, day of the month, date

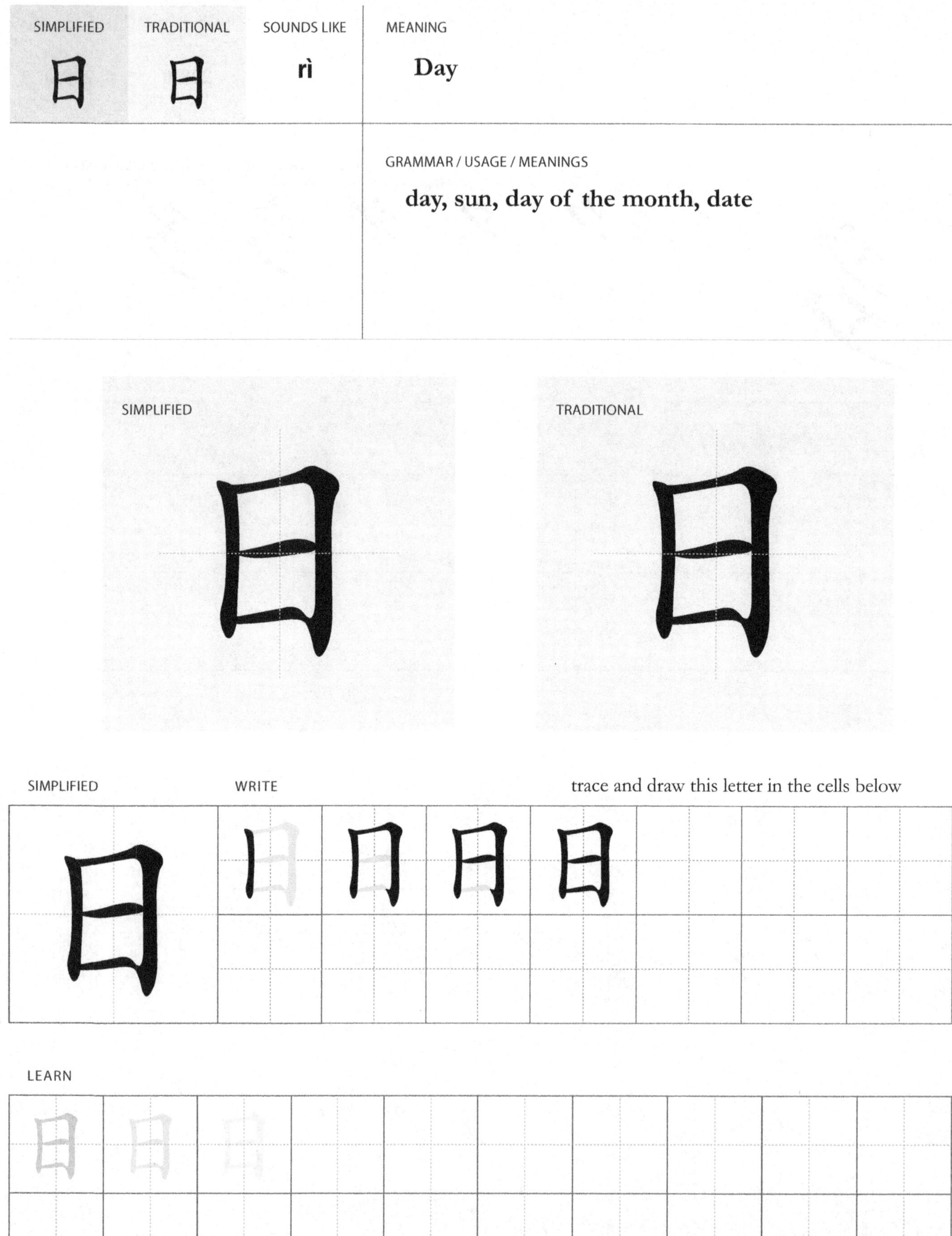

UNICODE SIM.	UNICODE TRAD.
26085	**26085**

TRADITIONAL

日

WRITE

trace and draw this letter in the cells below

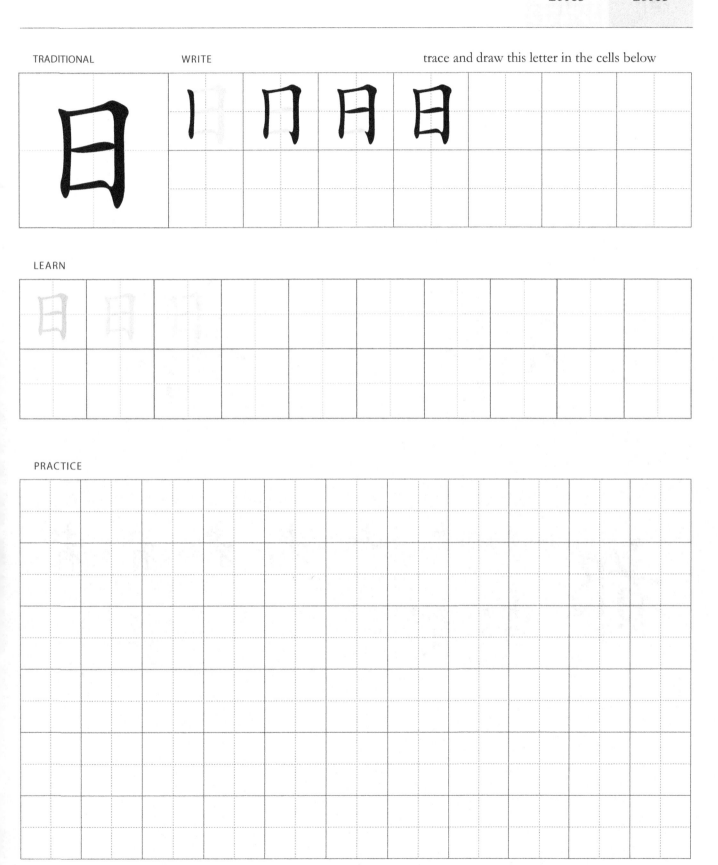

丨 冂 闩 日

LEARN

日 日 日

PRACTICE

SIMPLIFIED	TRADITIONAL	SOUNDS LIKE	MEANING
都	都	dōu	Both

GRAMMAR / USAGE / MEANINGS

all, both (if two things are involved), already, just because of, even, entirely (due to) each

SIMPLIFIED

都

TRADITIONAL

都

SIMPLIFIED

WRITE

trace and draw this letter in the cells below

都

LEARN

UNICODE SIM.	UNICODE TRAD.
37117	37117

TRADITIONAL

都

WRITE

trace and draw this letter in the cells below

一 十 土 耂 者 者 者 都 都

LEARN

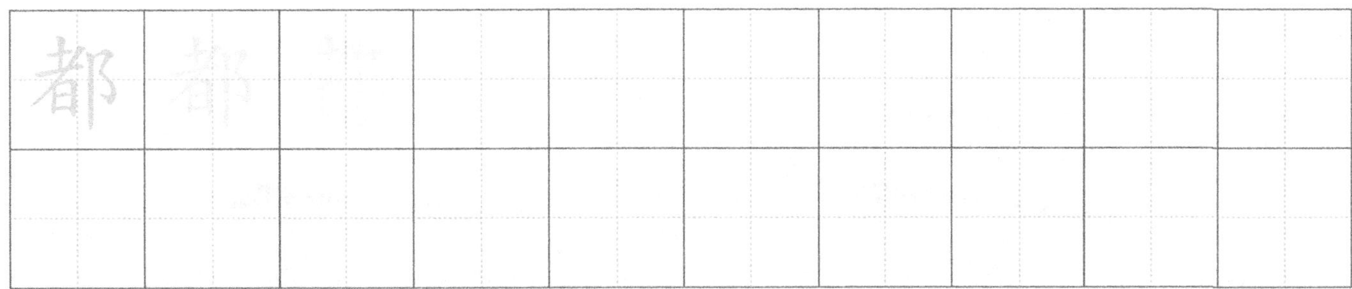

PRACTICE

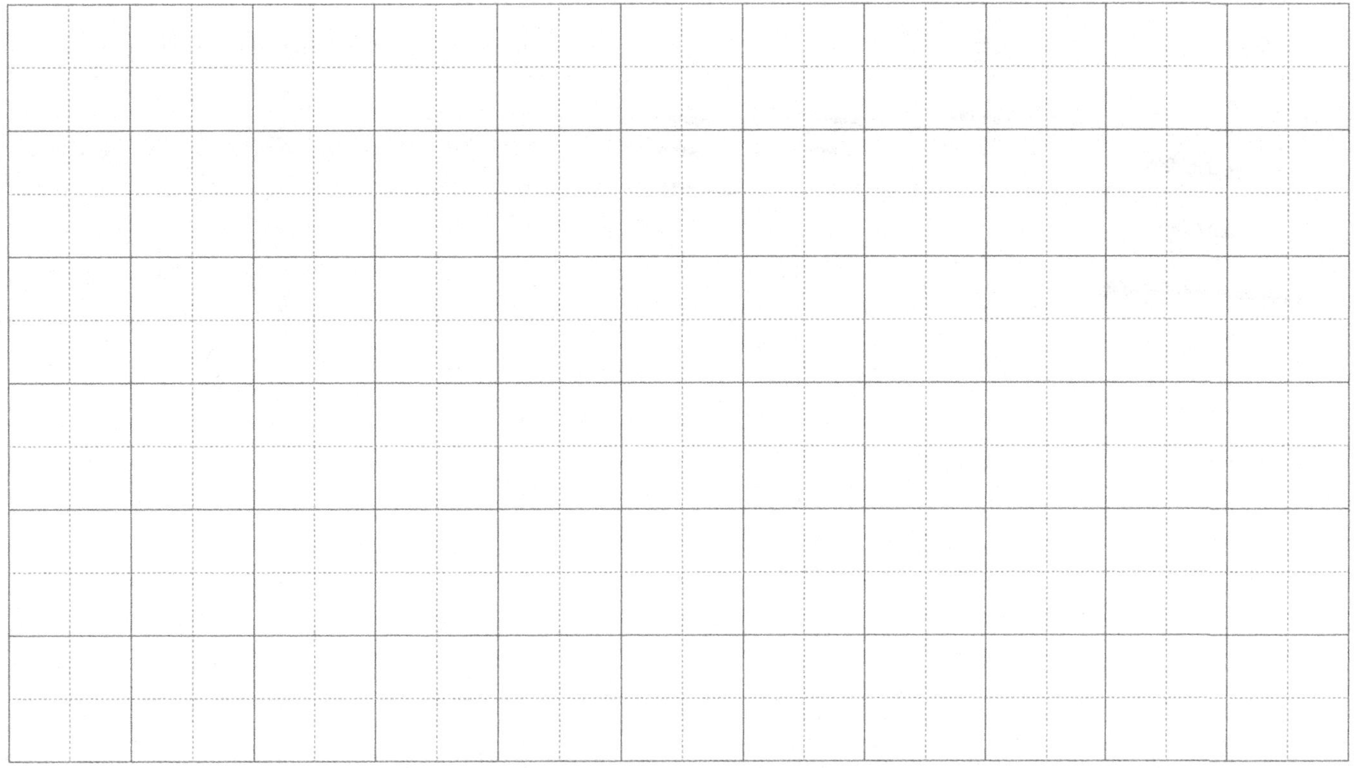

SIMPLIFIED	TRADITIONAL	SOUNDS LIKE	MEANING
三	三	**sān**	**Three**

GRAMMAR / USAGE / MEANINGS

three, many

SIMPLIFIED

三

TRADITIONAL

三

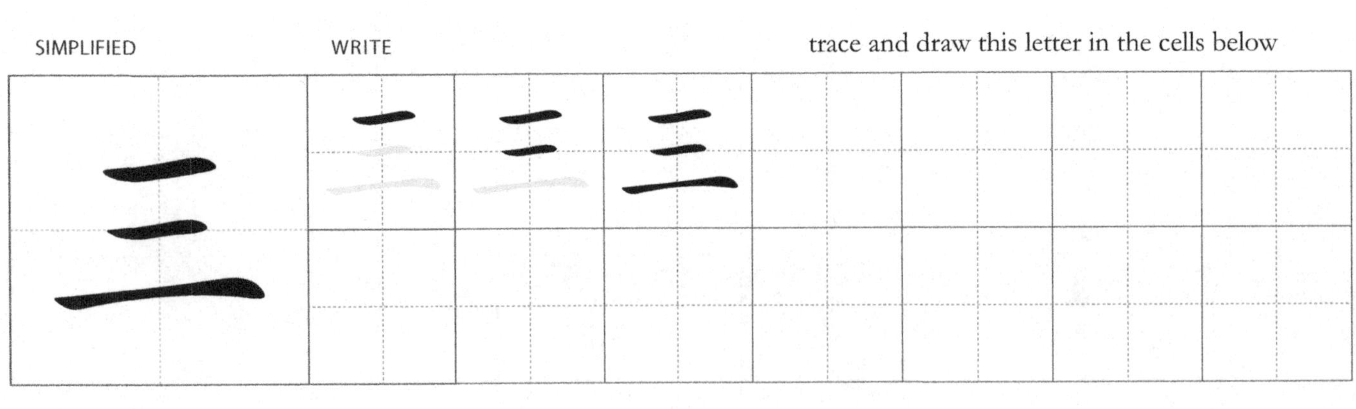

SIMPLIFIED

三

WRITE

trace and draw this letter in the cells below

LEARN

UNICODE SIM.	UNICODE TRAD.
19977	**19977**

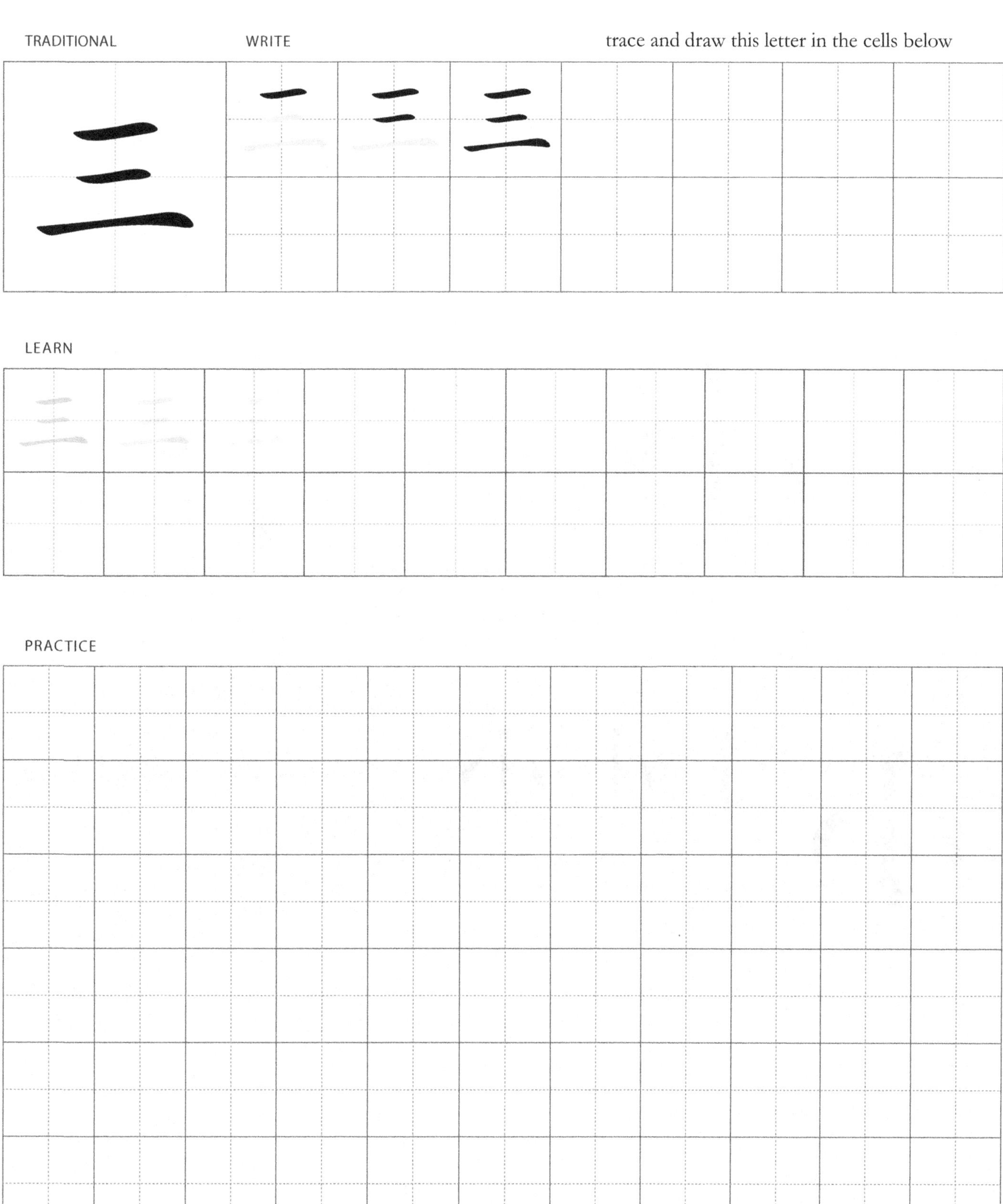

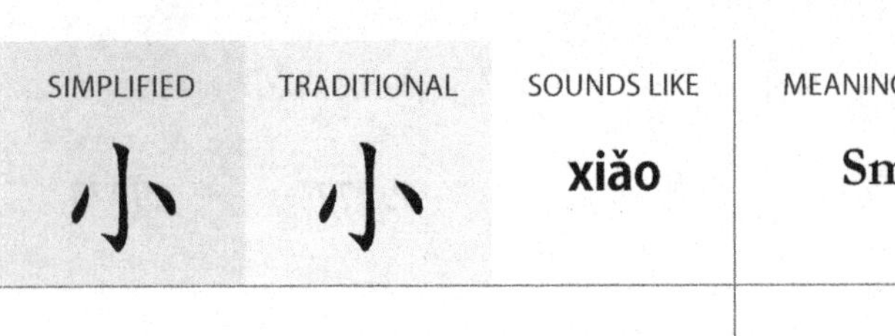

MEANING

Small

GRAMMAR / USAGE / MEANINGS

small, the young, few, tiny, young

SIMPLIFIED

WRITE

trace and draw this letter in the cells below

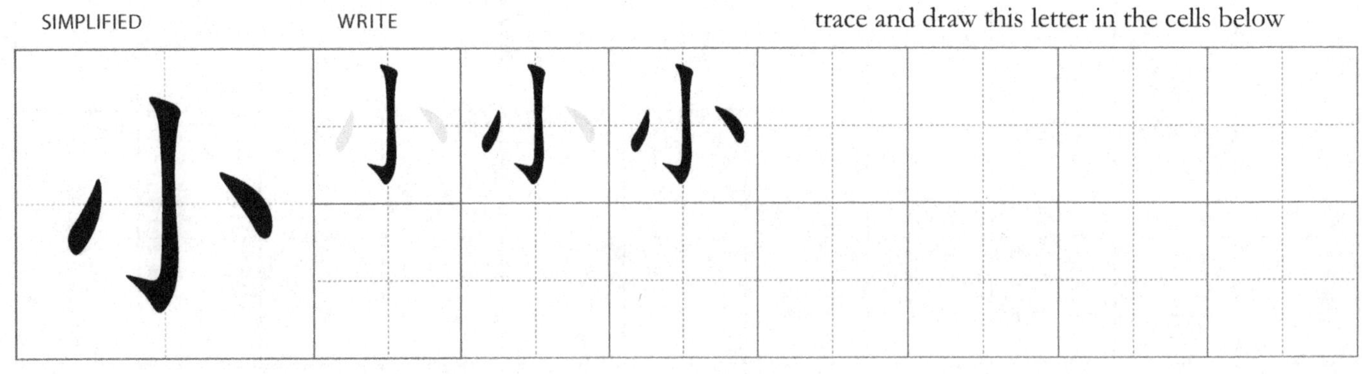

LEARN

UNICODE SIM.	UNICODE TRAD.
23567	23567

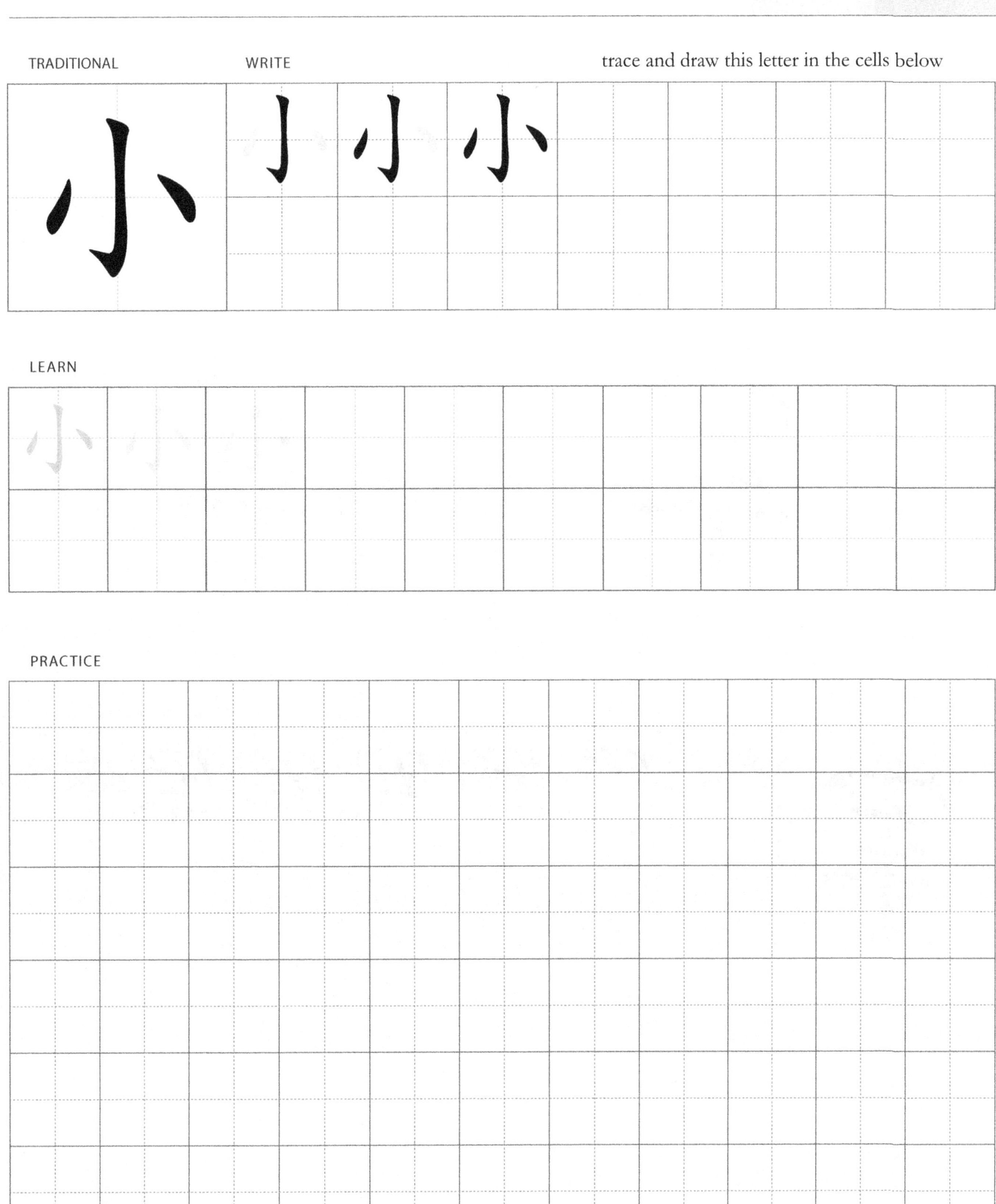

SIMPLIFIED	TRADITIONAL	SOUNDS LIKE	MEANING
军	軍	jūn	Military

GRAMMAR / USAGE / MEANINGS

army, arms, military

SIMPLIFIED

军

TRADITIONAL

軍

SIMPLIFIED

WRITE

trace and draw this letter in the cells below

LEARN

UNICODE SIM.	UNICODE TRAD.
20891	**36557**

TRADITIONAL

軍

WRITE

trace and draw this letter in the cells below

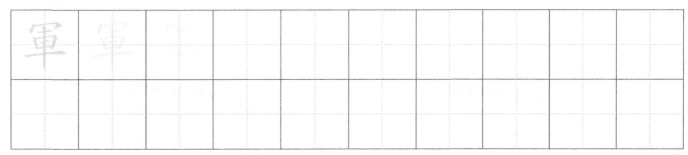

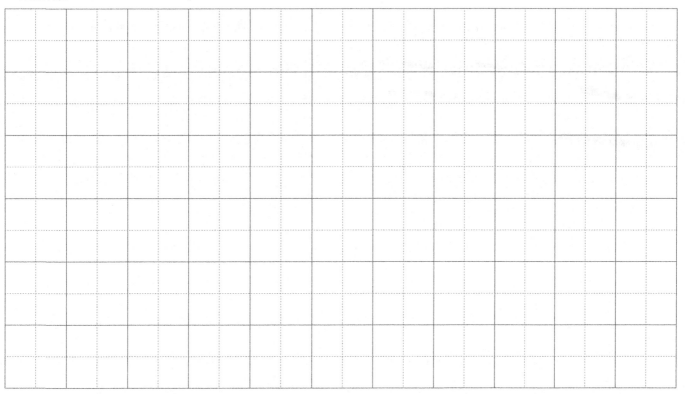

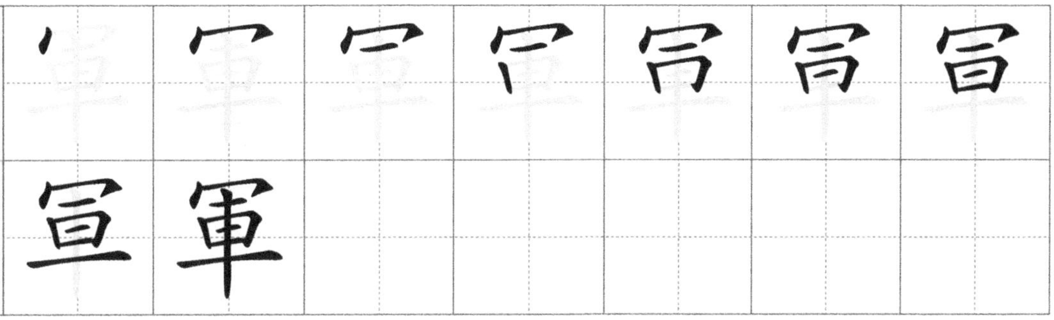

LEARN

PRACTICE

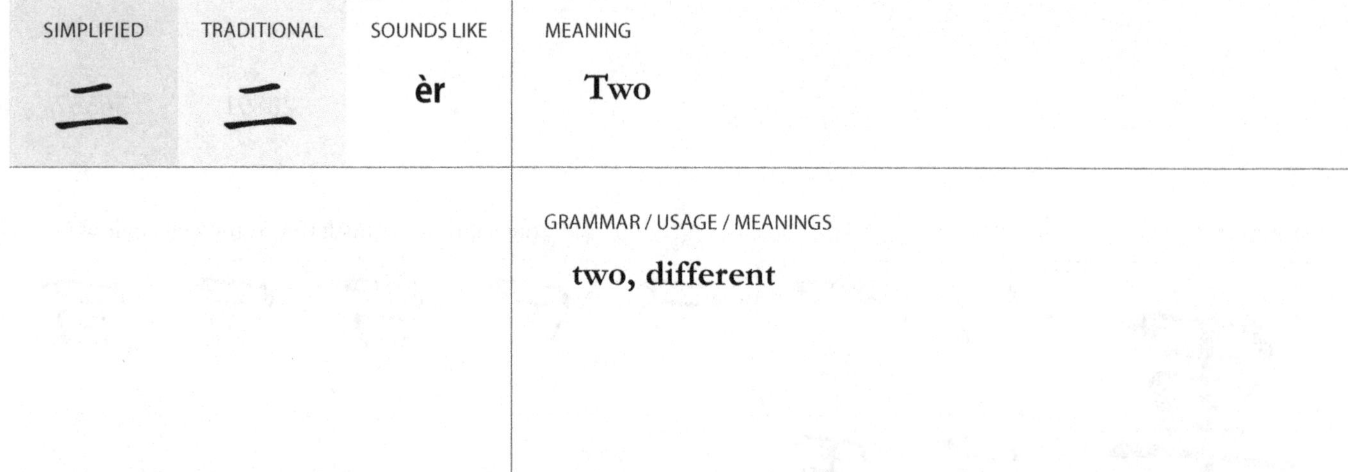
SIMPLIFIED 二 | TRADITIONAL 二 | SOUNDS LIKE **èr** | MEANING **Two**

GRAMMAR / USAGE / MEANINGS

two, different

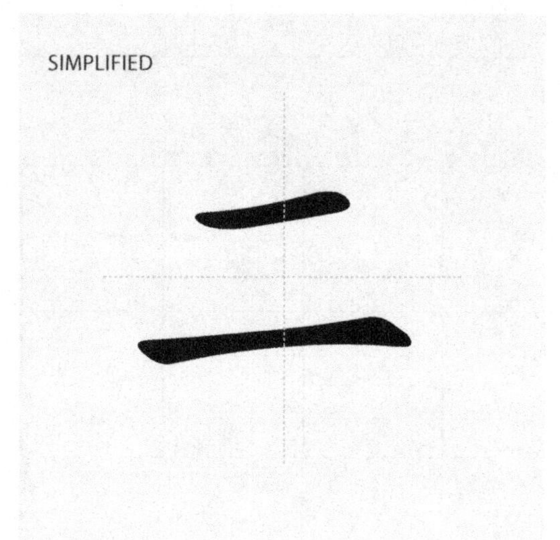

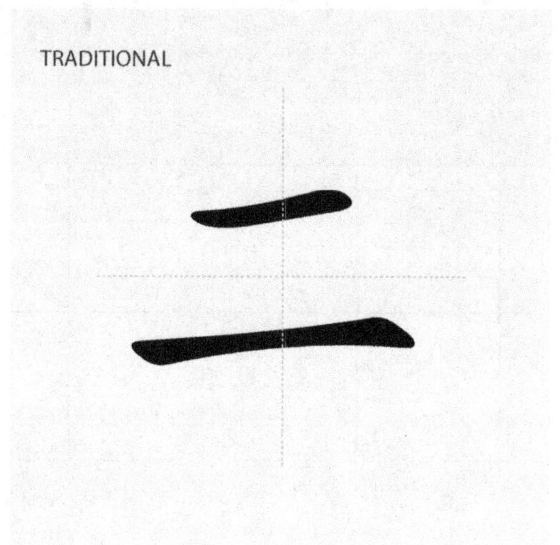

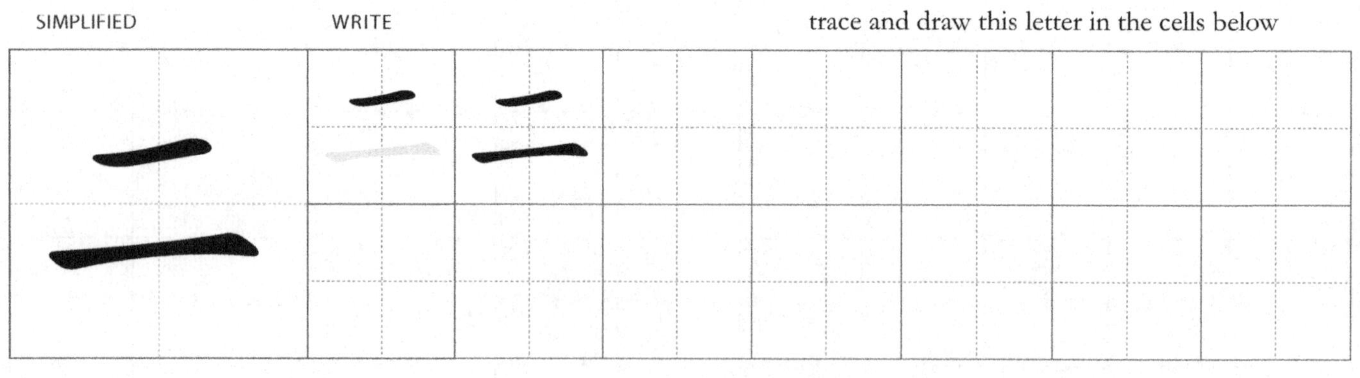

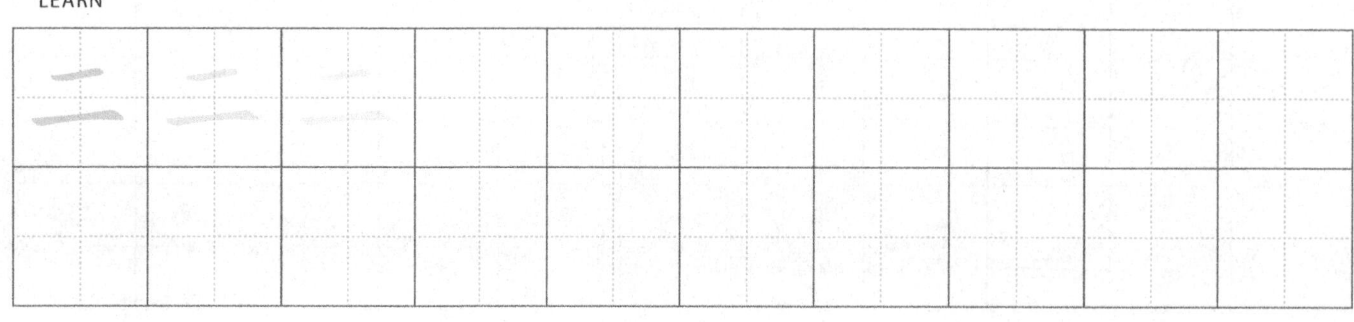

UNICODE SIM.	UNICODE TRAD.
20108	20108

TRADITIONAL

WRITE

trace and draw this letter in the cells below

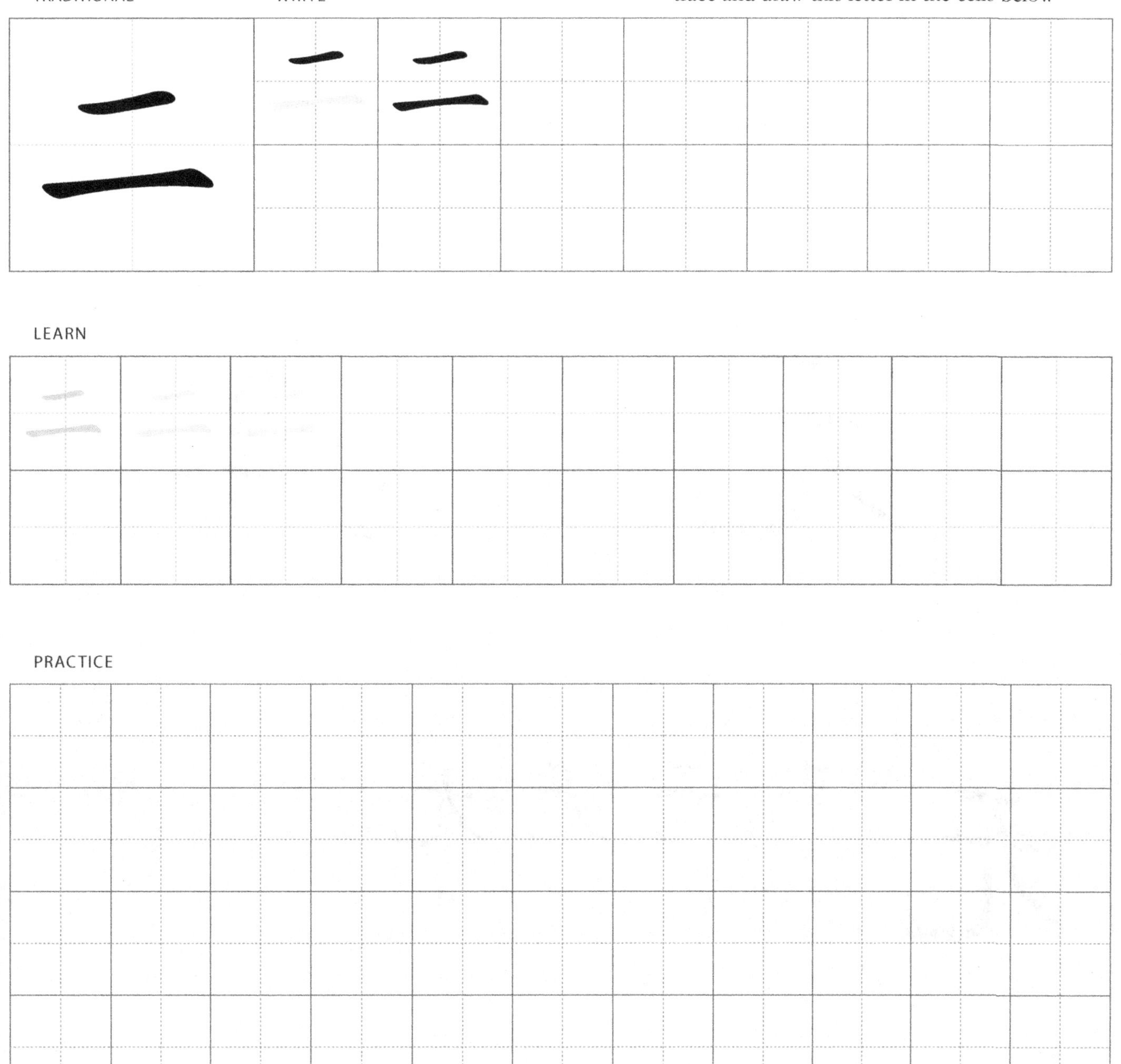

LEARN

PRACTICE

SIMPLIFIED	TRADITIONAL	SOUNDS LIKE	MEANING
无	無	**wú**	**None**

GRAMMAR / USAGE / MEANINGS

not to have, /less, regardless of, no, none, to lack, not, un/

SIMPLIFIED

无

TRADITIONAL

無

SIMPLIFIED　　WRITE　　trace and draw this letter in the cells below

LEARN

UNICODE SIM.	UNICODE TRAD.
26080	28961

TRADITIONAL

無

WRITE

trace and draw this letter in the cells below

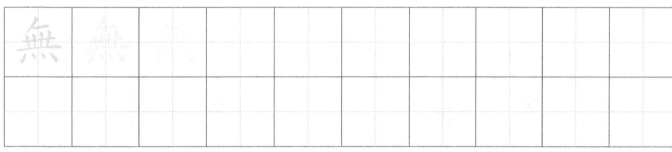

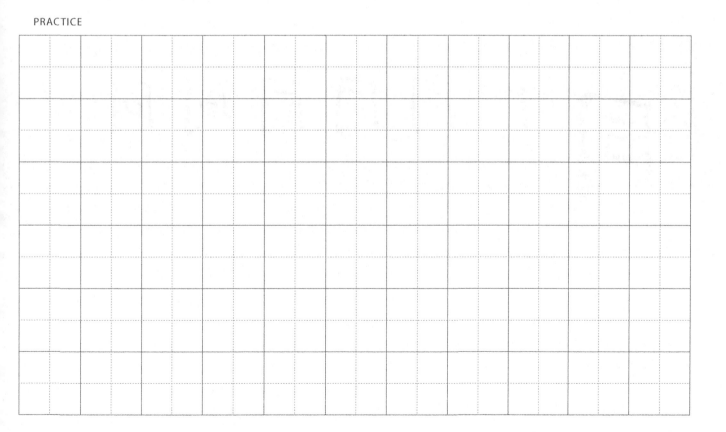

LEARN

PRACTICE

SIMPLIFIED	TRADITIONAL	SOUNDS LIKE	MEANING
同	同	tóng	Same

GRAMMAR / USAGE / MEANINGS

same, like,similar, with, as , together, alike

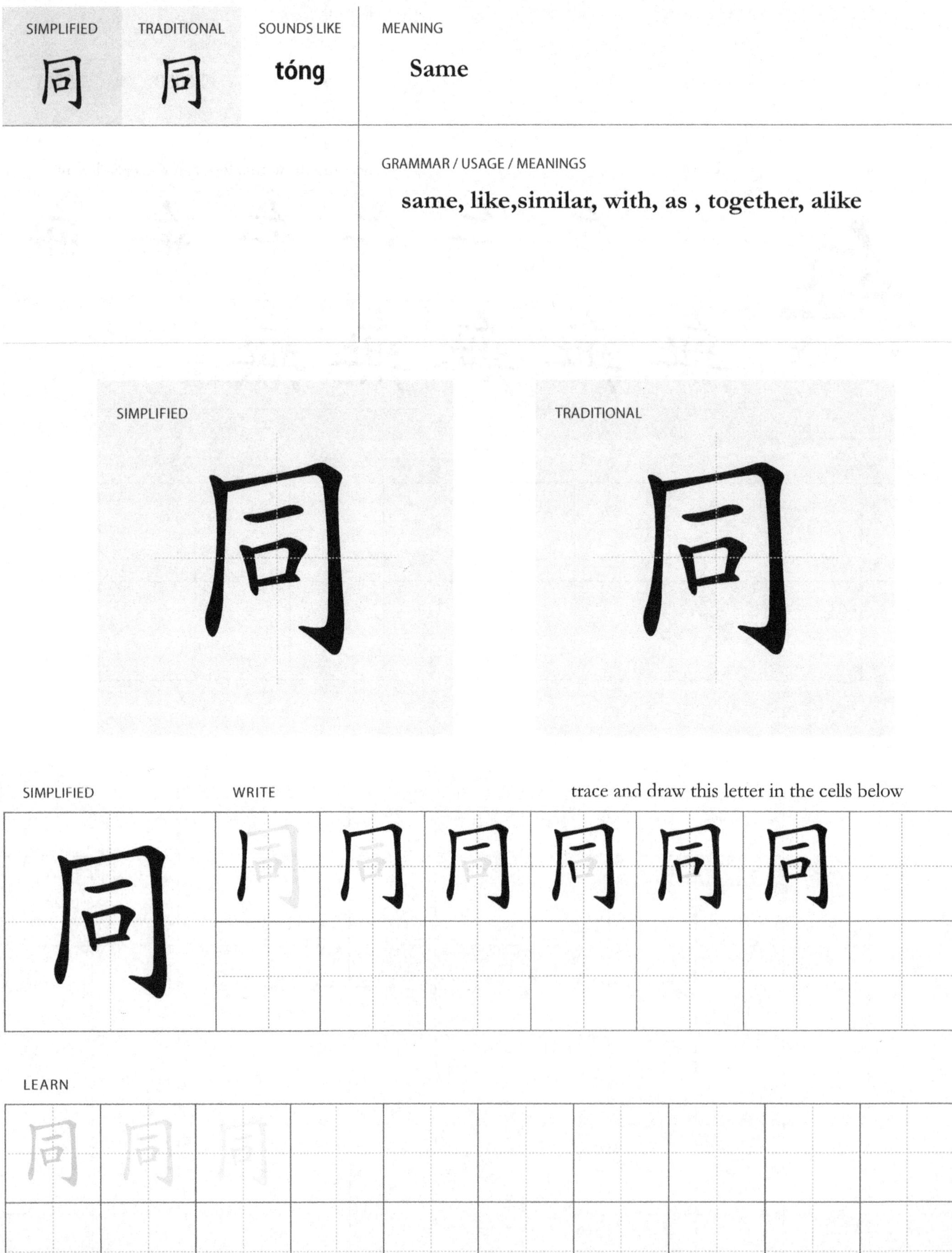

UNICODE SIM.	UNICODE TRAD.
21516	21516

TRADITIONAL

同

WRITE

trace and draw this letter in the cells below

丨 冂 冃 同 同 同

LEARN

同 同

PRACTICE

SIMPLIFIED	TRADITIONAL	SOUNDS LIKE	MEANING
么	麼	me	What?

GRAMMAR / USAGE / MEANINGS

(interrog. suff.)

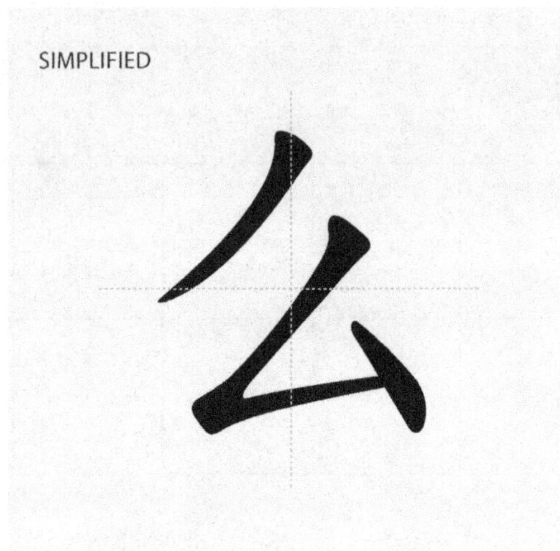

TRADITIONAL

麼

SIMPLIFIED WRITE trace and draw this letter in the cells below

LEARN

UNICODE SIM.	UNICODE TRAD.
20040	40636

TRADITIONAL

麼

WRITE

trace and draw this letter in the cells below

LEARN

PRACTICE

SIMPLIFIED	TRADITIONAL	SOUNDS LIKE	MEANING
经	經	jīng	Through

GRAMMAR / USAGE / MEANINGS

longitude, scripture, sacred book, menstruation, pass through, to manage, to undergo, to endure, as a result of, regular, classics

TRADITIONAL

經

SIMPLIFIED WRITE trace and draw this letter in the cells below

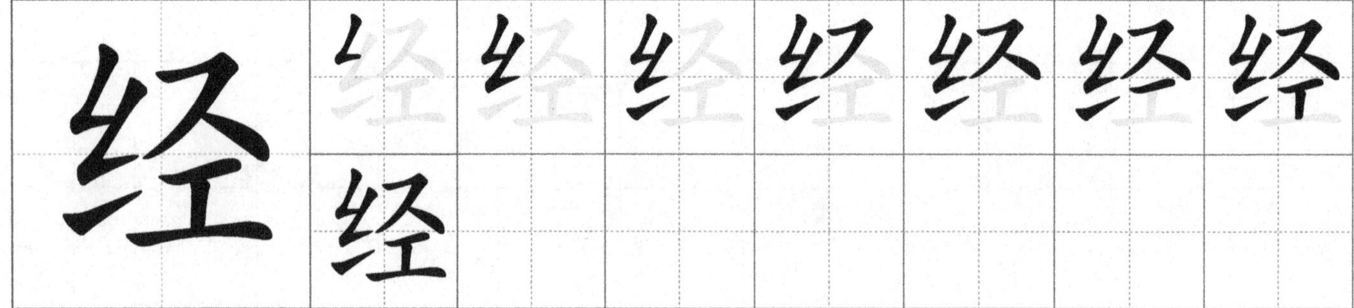

LEARN

UNICODE SIM.	UNICODE TRAD.
32463	32147

TRADITIONAL

經

WRITE

trace and draw this letter in the cells below

LEARN

經 經 經

PRACTICE

SIMPLIFIED
TRADITIONAL
SOUNDS LIKE
MEANING
法
法
fǎ
Law
GRAMMAR / USAGE / MEANINGS
law, follow, method, way, standard, Buddhist teaching
SIMPLIFIED
法
TRADITIONAL
法
SIMPLIFIED
WRITE
tracc and draw this letter in the cells below
法
LEARN

UNICODE SIM.	UNICODE TRAD.
27861	**27861**

TRADITIONAL

WRITE

trace and draw this letter in the cells below

法

法

LEARN

PRACTICE

SIMPLIFIED	TRADITIONAL	SOUNDS LIKE	MEANING
当	當	dāng / dàng	When

GRAMMAR / USAGE / MEANINGS

to be, to act as, replace, manage, represent, when, withstand, during, should, ought, match equally, same, adequate, equal, fitting, proper, obstruct, just at (a time or place), on the spot, to pawn, suitable, right, just at / at or in the very same…

TRADITIONAL

當

SIMPLIFIED WRITE trace and draw this letter in the cells below

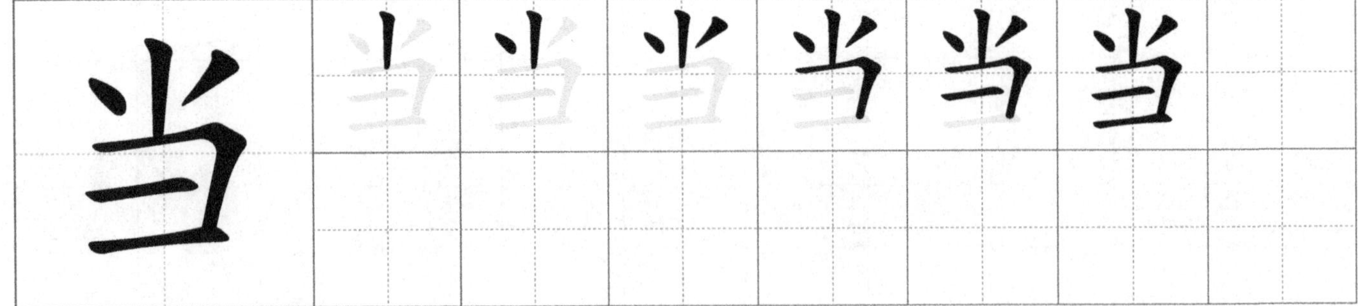

LEARN

UNICODE SIM.	UNICODE TRAD.
24403	30070

TRADITIONAL

當

WRITE

trace and draw this letter in the cells below

LEARN

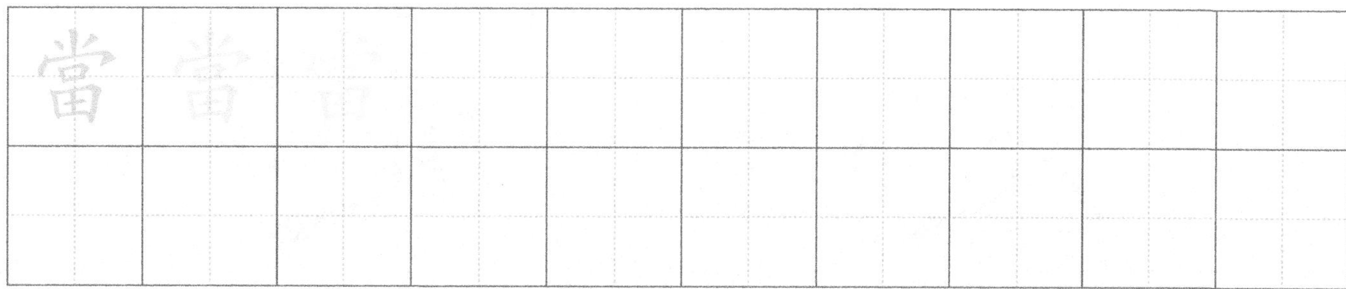

PRACTICE

SIMPLIFIED	TRADITIONAL	SOUNDS LIKE	MEANING
起	起	qǐ	Start

GRAMMAR / USAGE / MEANINGS

to raise, to rise, to get up, to begin, case, to remove, to grow, to draft, to build

SIMPLIFIED

起

TRADITIONAL

起

SIMPLIFIED WRITE trace and draw this letter in the cells below

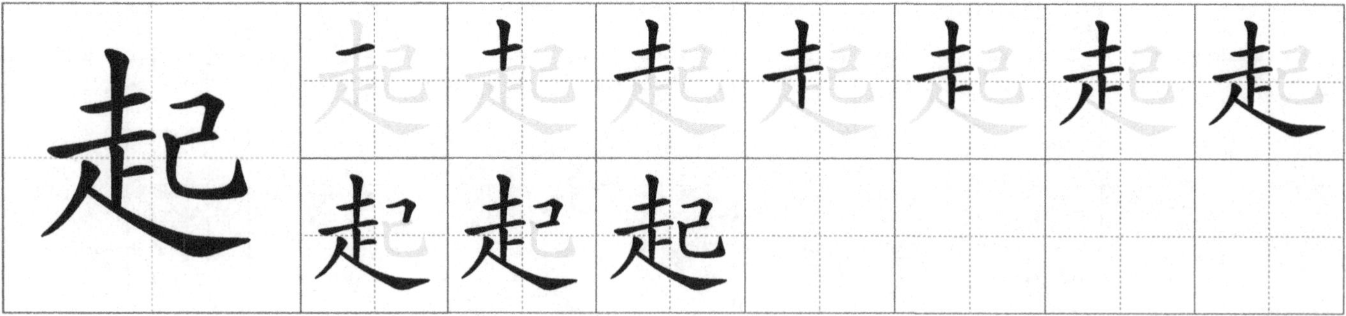

LEARN

UNICODE SIM.	UNICODE TRAD.
36215	36215

TRADITIONAL

起

WRITE

trace and draw this letter in the cells below

一 十 土 丰 丰 走 走 起 起 起

LEARN

起 起 起

PRACTICE

SIMPLIFIED	TRADITIONAL	SOUNDS LIKE	MEANING
与	與	yú / yǔ / yù	With

GRAMMAR / USAGE / MEANINGS

to give, and, together with / take part in, to support, (interrog. part.)

SIMPLIFIED

与

TRADITIONAL

與

SIMPLIFIED　　WRITE　　trace and draw this letter in the cells below

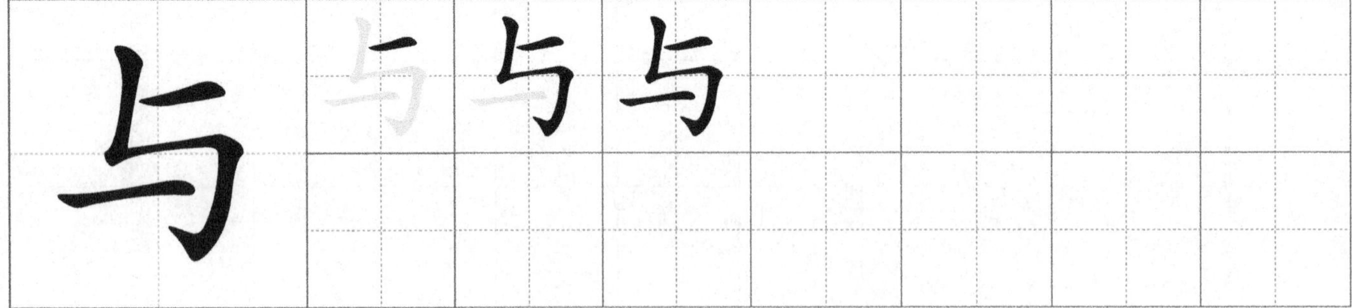

LEARN

与 与 与

UNICODE SIM.	UNICODE TRAD.
19982	33287

TRADITIONAL

與

WRITE

trace and draw this letter in the cells below

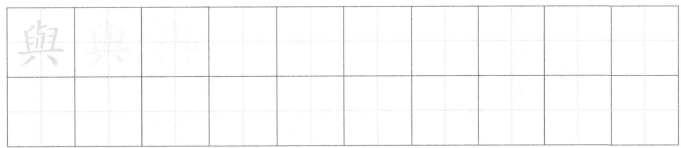

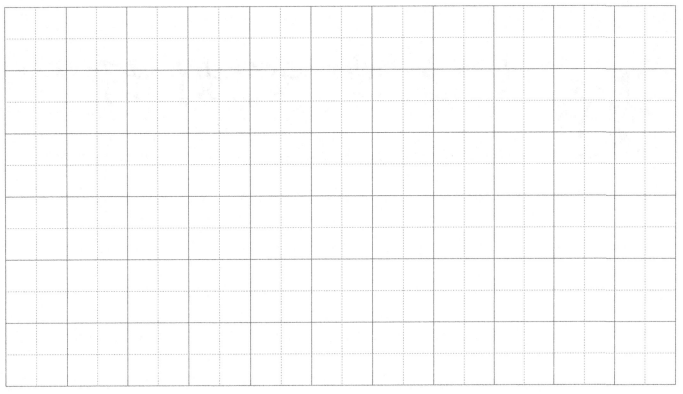

LEARN

PRACTICE

SIMPLIFIED	TRADITIONAL	SOUNDS LIKE	MEANING
好	好	**hǎo / hào**	**Good**

GRAMMAR / USAGE / MEANINGS

good, be in good health, friendly, be convenient, love / be fond of, be liable to

SIMPLIFIED

好

TRADITIONAL

好

SIMPLIFIED

WRITE

trace and draw this letter in the cells below

好

LEARN

好 好 好

UNICODE SIM.	UNICODE TRAD.
22909	22909

TRADITIONAL

好

WRITE

trace and draw this letter in the cells below

LEARN

PRACTICE

SIMPLIFIED	TRADITIONAL	SOUNDS LIKE	MEANING
看	看	kān / kàn	Watch

GRAMMAR / USAGE / MEANINGS

to take care of, to look after, depend on, to guard / it depends, to watch, watch out, think, to read, to see/visit, to look at, to judge, regard, to treat

SIMPLIFIED

看

TRADITIONAL

看

SIMPLIFIED WRITE tracc and draw this letter in the cells below

LEARN

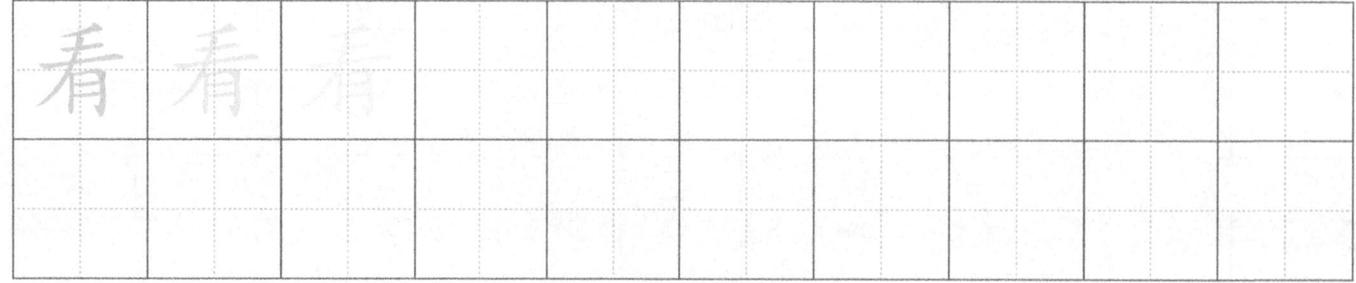

UNICODE SIM.	UNICODE TRAD.
30475	30475

TRADITIONAL

看

WRITE

trace and draw this letter in the cells below

看 看

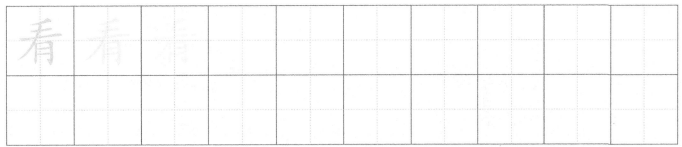

LEARN

PRACTICE

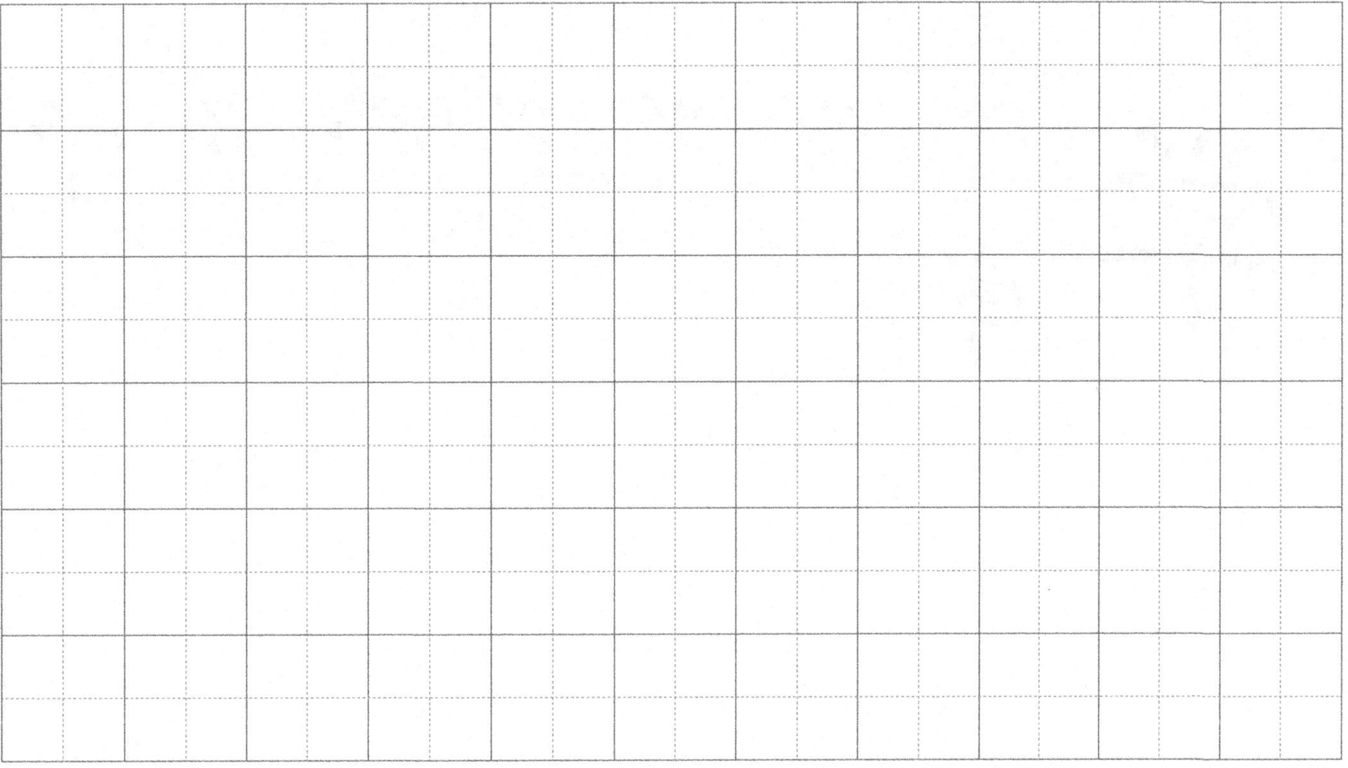

SIMPLIFIED	TRADITIONAL	SOUNDS LIKE	MEANING
学	學	**xué**	Learning

GRAMMAR / USAGE / MEANINGS

learn, study, mimic, learning, knowledge, subject of study, school, college

TRADITIONAL

學

SIMPLIFIED

WRITE

trace and draw this letter in the cells below

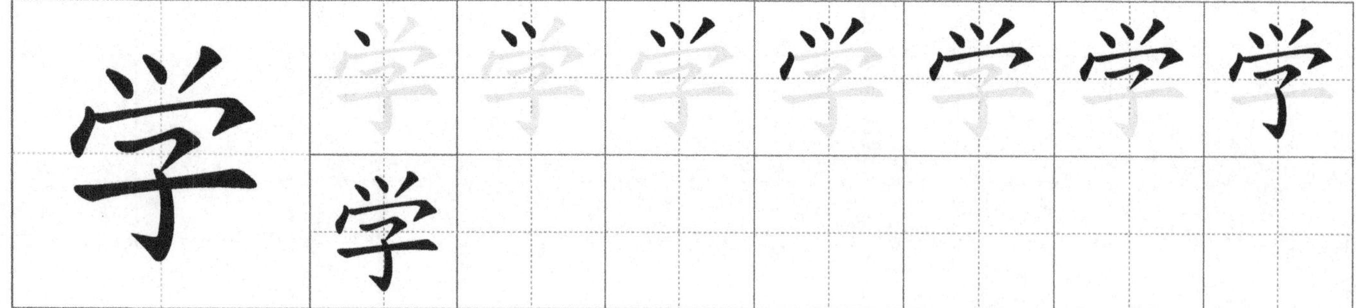

LEARN

UNICODE SIM.	UNICODE TRAD.
23398	23416

TRADITIONAL

學

WRITE

trace and draw this letter in the cells below

LEARN

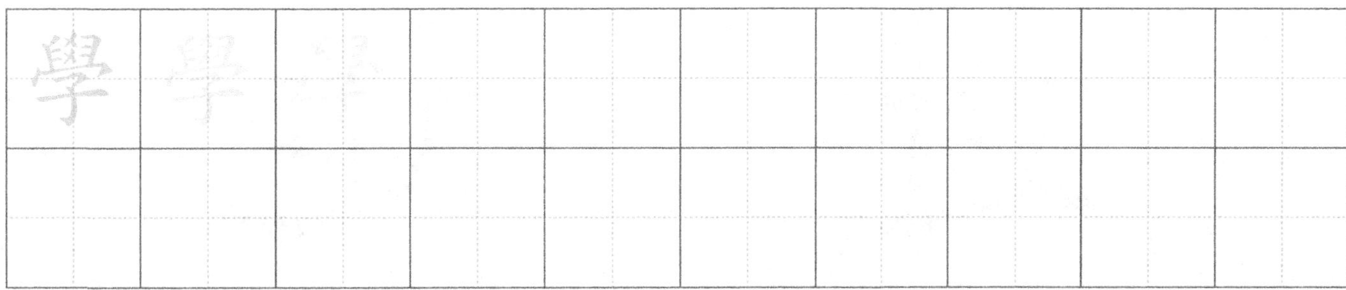

PRACTICE

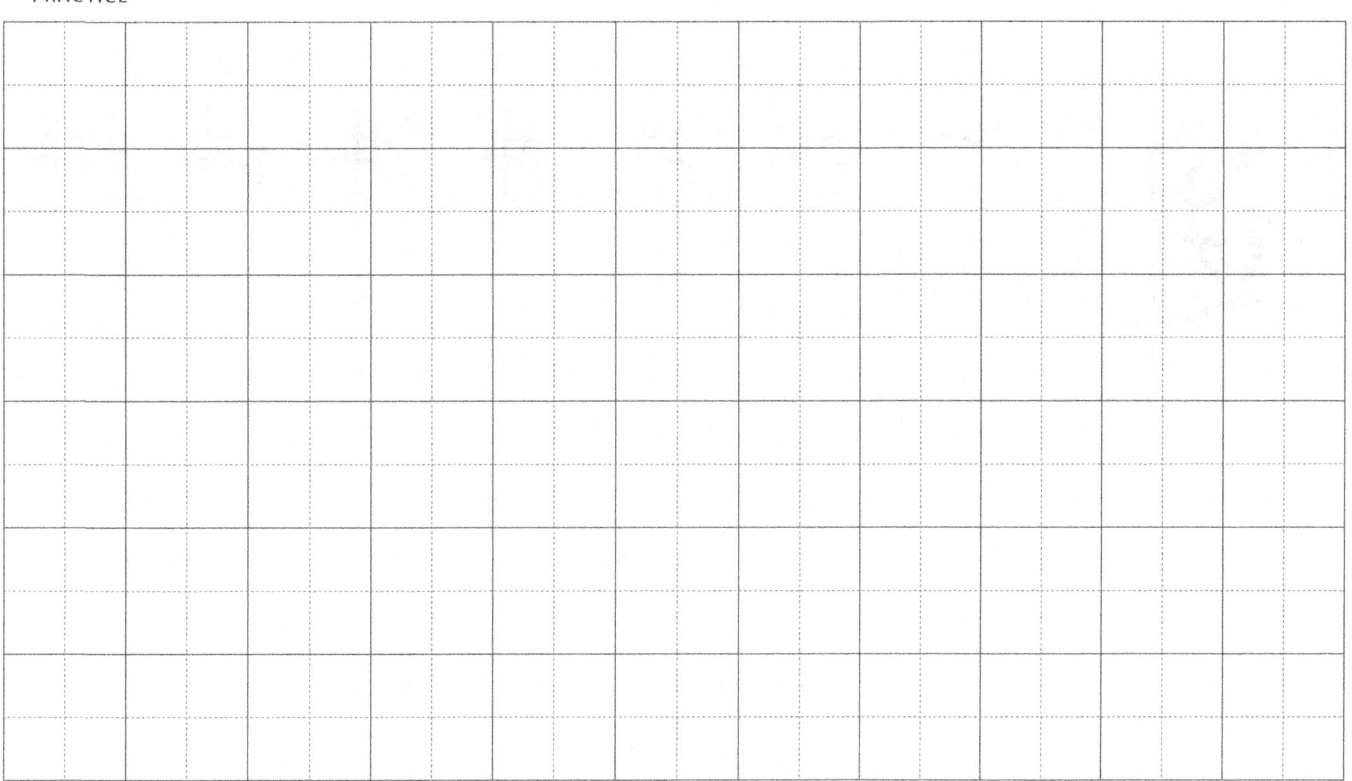

SIMPLIFIED	TRADITIONAL	SOUNDS LIKE	MEANING
进	進	jin	Enter

GRAMMAR / USAGE / MEANINGS

advance, score a goal, enter, submit, to come in, receive, eat, drink

TRADITIONAL

進

SIMPLIFIED

WRITE

trace and draw this letter in the cells below

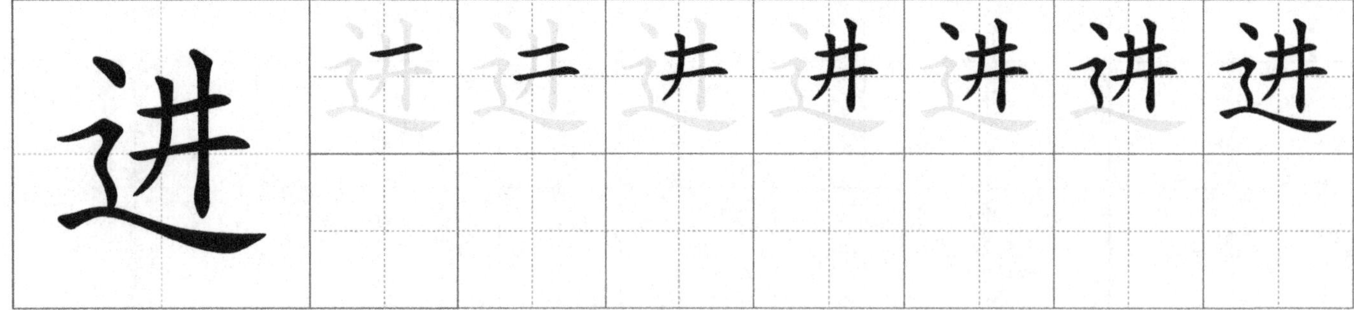

LEARN

UNICODE SIM.	UNICODE TRAD.
36827	36914

TRADITIONAL

進

WRITE

trace and draw this letter in the cells below

丿 亻 亻 亻 亻 亻 隹 隹 ⻌隹 ⻌隹 進

LEARN

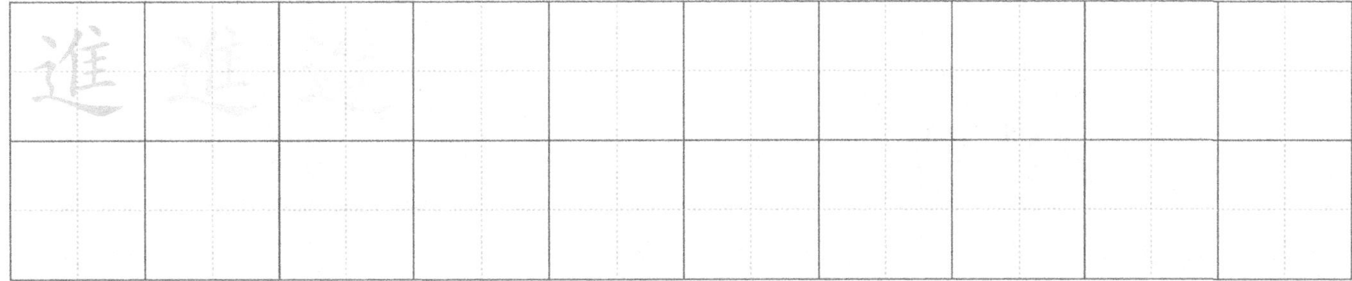

PRACTICE

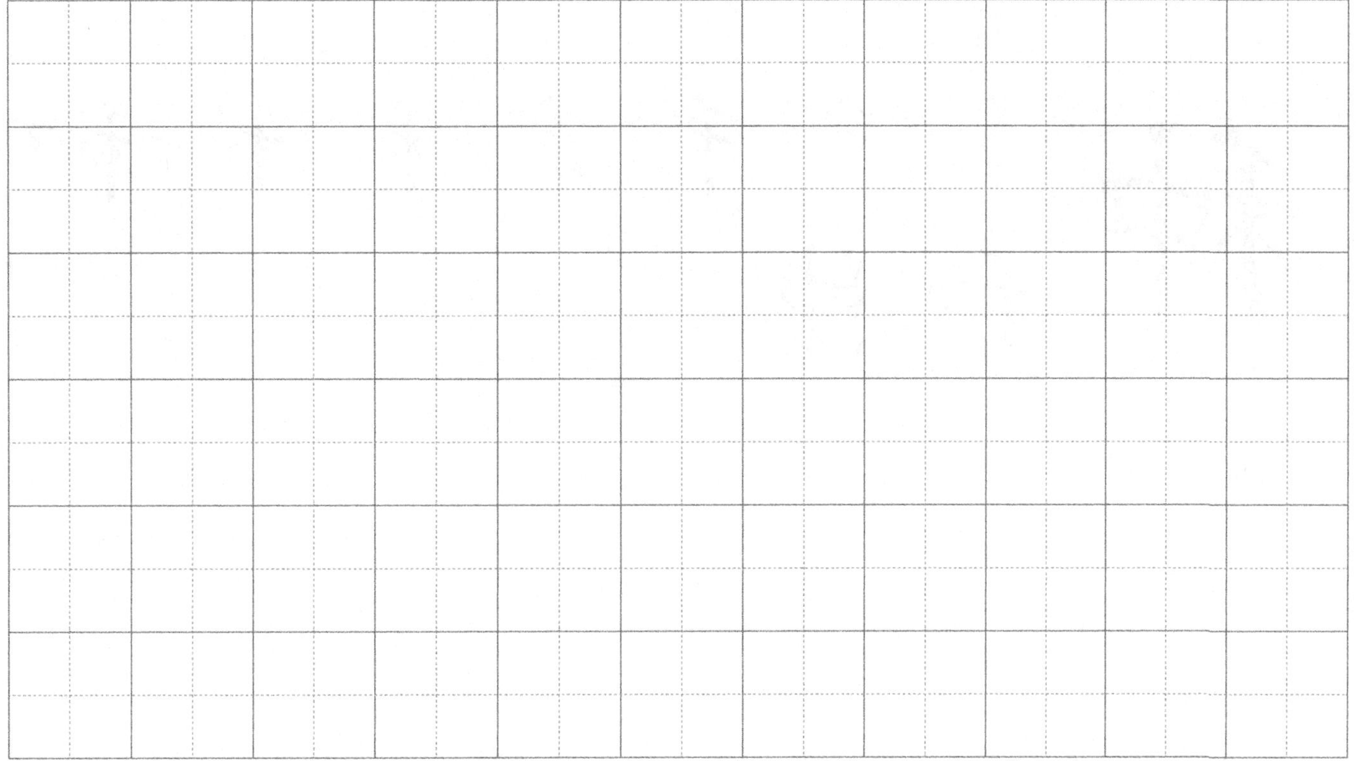

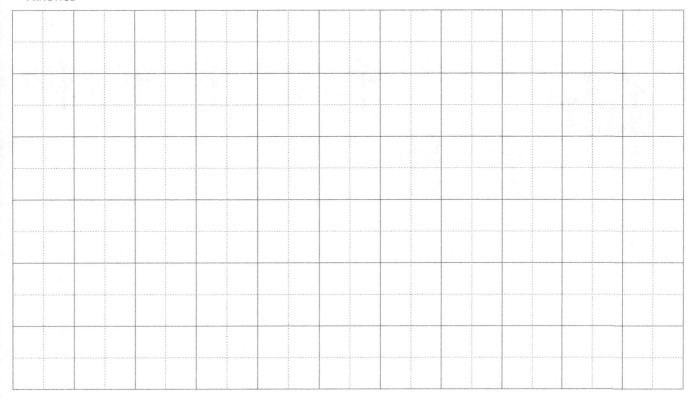

SIMPLIFIED	TRADITIONAL	SOUNDS LIKE	MEANING
种	種	**zhǒng / zhòng**	**Species**

GRAMMAR / USAGE / MEANINGS

kind, type, species, race (of people), to plant, seed, grit, type / to grow

SIMPLIFIED

TRADITIONAL

種

SIMPLIFIED

种

WRITE

trace and draw this letter in the cells below

LEARN

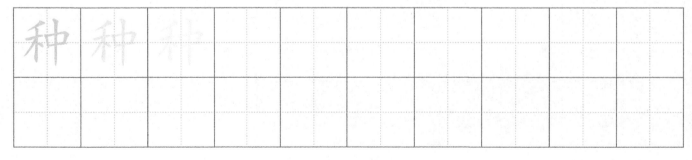

UNICODE SIM.	UNICODE TRAD.
31181	31278

TRADITIONAL

種

WRITE

trace and draw this letter in the cells below

LEARN

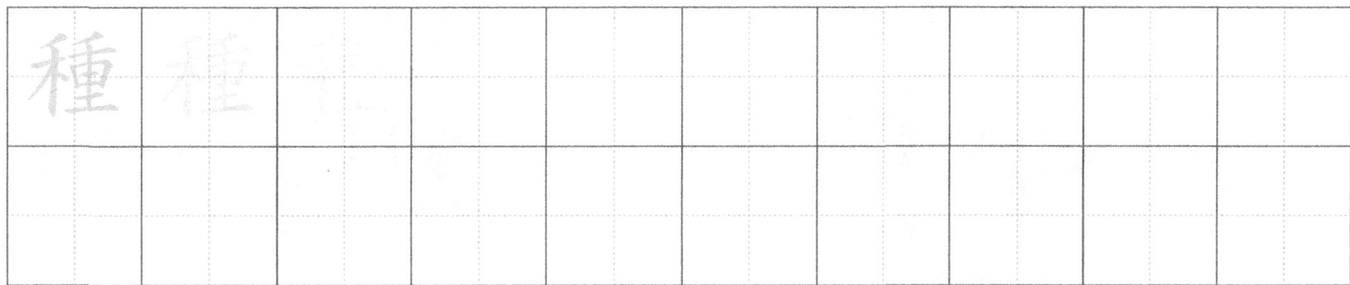

PRACTICE

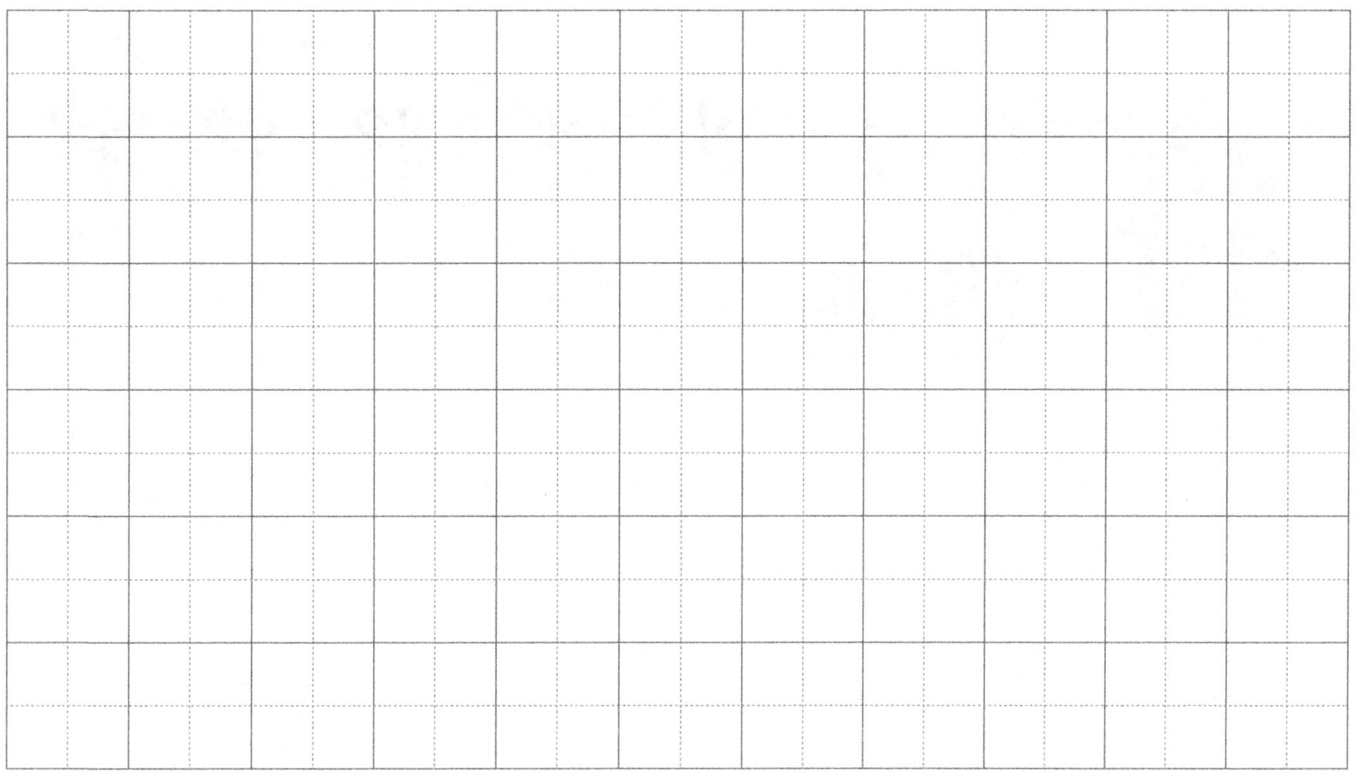

SIMPLIFIED	TRADITIONAL	SOUNDS LIKE	MEANING
将	將	jiāng / jiàng	Will

GRAMMAR / USAGE / MEANINGS

ready, to get, prepared, to use / a general, (will, shall, future tense)

SIMPLIFIED

将

TRADITIONAL

將

SIMPLIFIED WRITE trace and draw this letter in the cells below

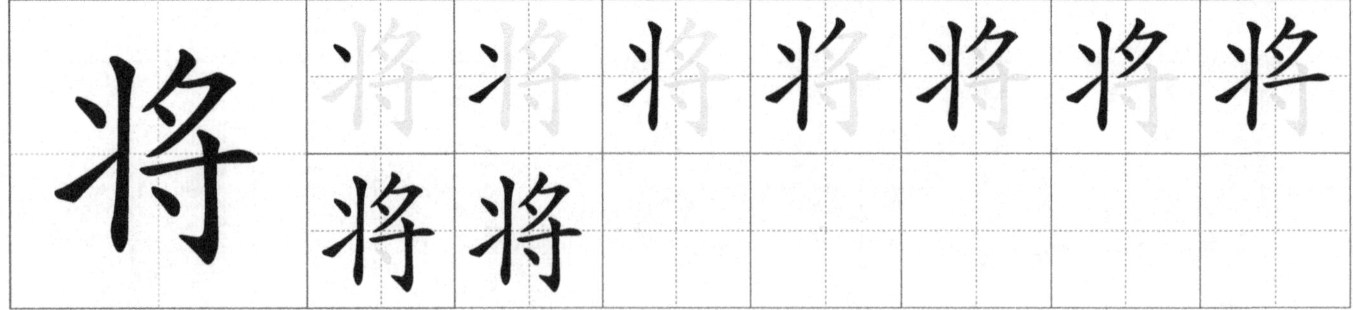

LEARN

UNICODE SIM.	UNICODE TRAD.
23558	23559

TRADITIONAL

將

WRITE

trace and draw this letter in the cells below

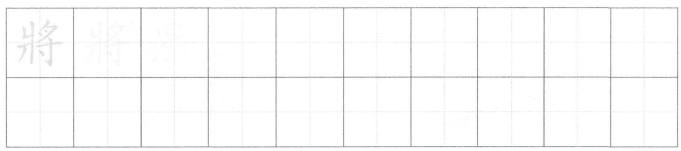

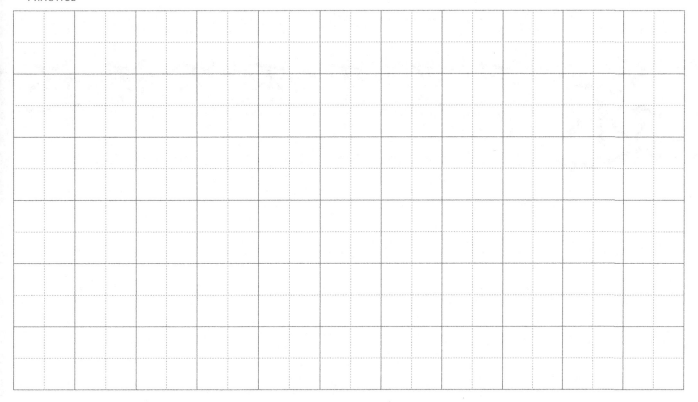

LEARN

PRACTICE

SIMPLIFIED	TRADITIONAL	SOUNDS LIKE	MEANING
还	還	**hái / huán**	**Also**

GRAMMAR / USAGE / MEANINGS

also, in addition, pay back, return, still, fairly, more, else, still, yet, (not) yet / (surname)

SIMPLIFIED

TRADITIONAL

SIMPLIFIED WRITE trace and draw this letter in the cells below

LEARN

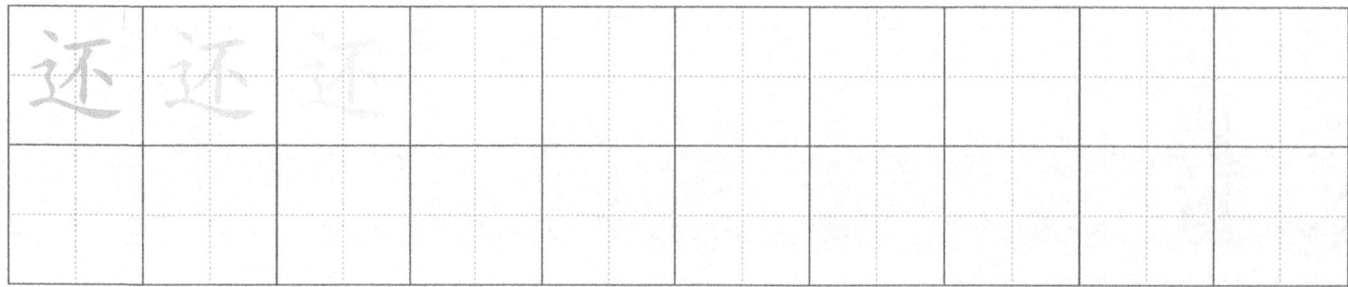

UNICODE SIM.	UNICODE TRAD.
36824	36996

TRADITIONAL

還

WRITE

trace and draw this letter in the cells below

LEARN

PRACTICE

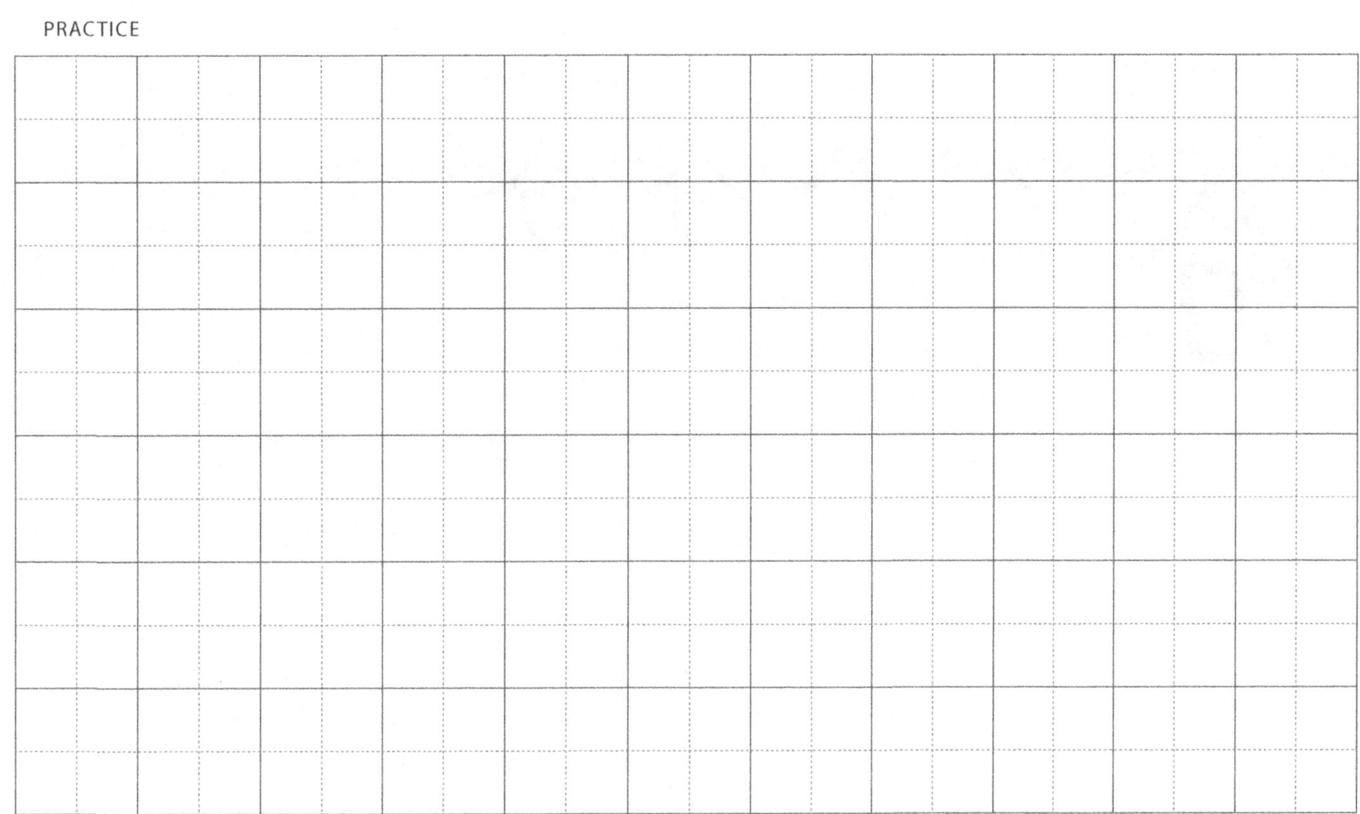

SIMPLIFIED	TRADITIONAL	SOUNDS LIKE	MEANING
分	分	fēn / fèn	Points

GRAMMAR / USAGE / MEANINGS

to divide, to distribute, to distinguish, minute, branch (of an organization), point/mark, fraction, (a measure word), one-tenth, a fractional unit of money in China, (a unit of length = 0.33centimeter) / part, component, what is within one's duty or rights

SIMPLIFIED WRITE trace and draw this letter in the cells below

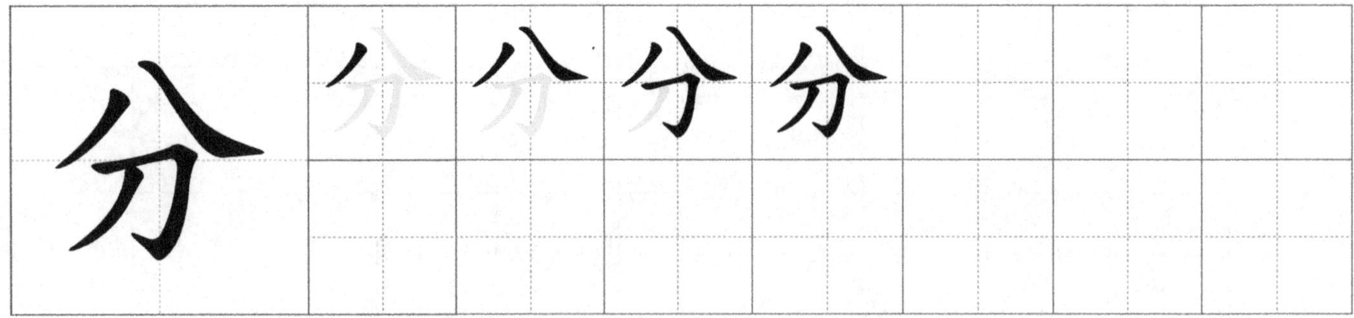

LEARN

分	分	分							

UNICODE SIM.	UNICODE TRAD.
20998	20998

TRADITIONAL

分

WRITE

trace and draw this letter in the cells below

丿 八 分 分

LEARN

分 分 分

PRACTICE

SIMPLIFIED	TRADITIONAL	SOUNDS LIKE	MEANING
此	此	cǐ	This

GRAMMAR / USAGE / MEANINGS

this, now, here

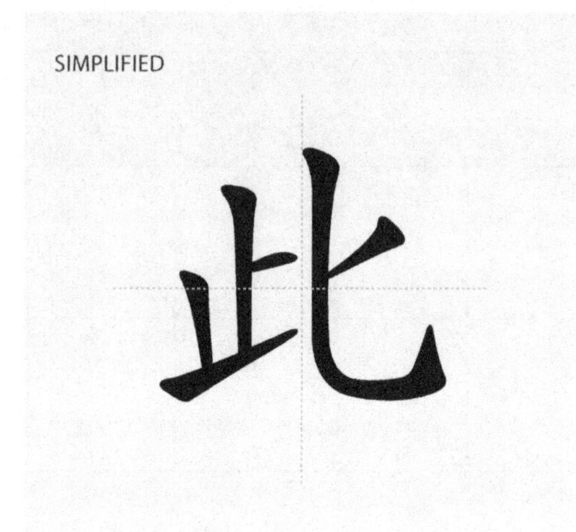

TRADITIONAL

此

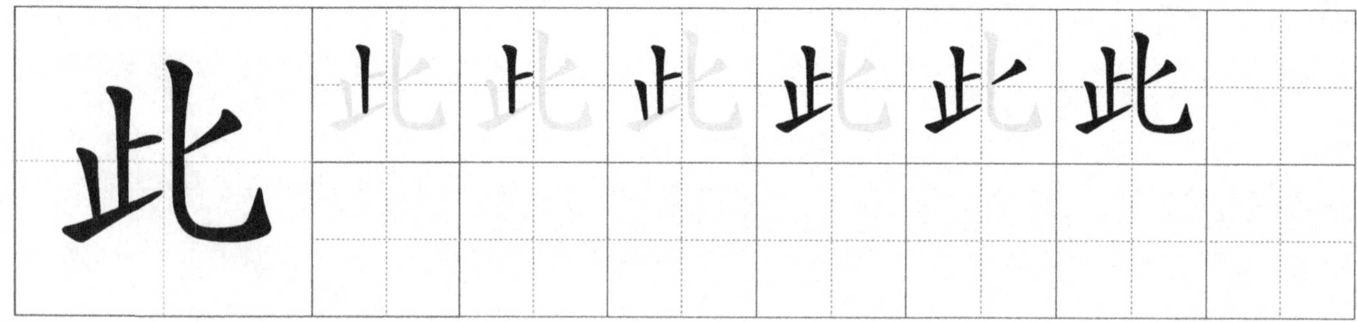

LEARN

UNICODE SIM.	UNICODE TRAD.
27492	**27492**

TRADITIONAL

此

WRITE

trace and draw this letter in the cells below

LEARN

PRACTICE

SIMPLIFIED	TRADITIONAL	SOUNDS LIKE	MEANING
心	心	xīn	**Heart**

GRAMMAR / USAGE / MEANINGS

the heart, heart, mind, center

SIMPLIFIED WRITE trace and draw this letter in the cells below

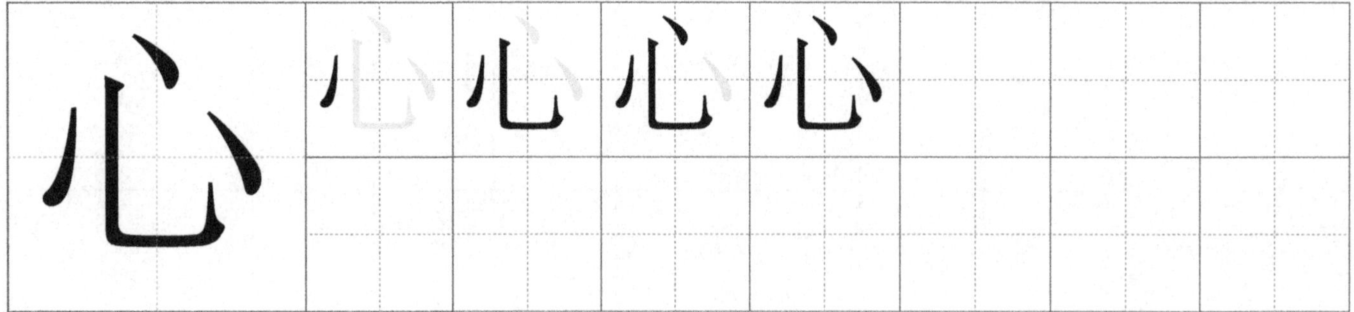

LEARN

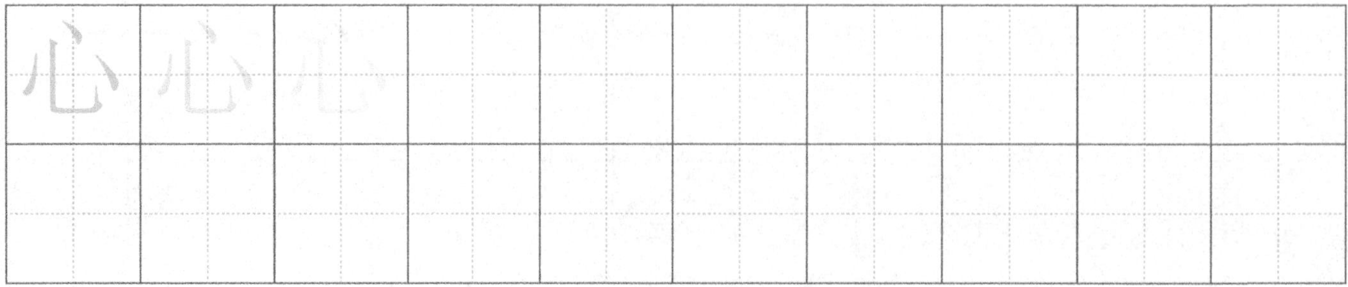

UNICODE SIM.	UNICODE TRAD.
24515	**24515**

TRADITIONAL

心

WRITE

trace and draw this letter in the cells below

丿 ⺅ 心 心

LEARN

心 心 心

PRACTICE

SIMPLIFIED	TRADITIONAL	SOUNDS LIKE	MEANING
前	前	qián	Front

GRAMMAR / USAGE / MEANINGS

before, go forward, in front, top, former, ago, earlier, previous, front, first

SIMPLIFIED

前

TRADITIONAL

前

SIMPLIFIED

WRITE

trace and draw this letter in the cells below

前

前 前 前 前 前 前 前

前 前

LEARN

前 前 前

UNICODE SIM.	UNICODE TRAD.
21069	21069

TRADITIONAL

前

WRITE

trace and draw this letter in the cells below

LEARN

PRACTICE

SIMPLIFIED	TRADITIONAL	SOUNDS LIKE	MEANING
麵	面	miàn	Noodles

GRAMMAR / USAGE / MEANINGS

face, extent, side, surface, powder, aspect, face, top, cover, flour, noodles, flour

SIMPLIFIED

麵

TRADITIONAL

面

SIMPLIFIED WRITE trace and draw this letter in the cells below

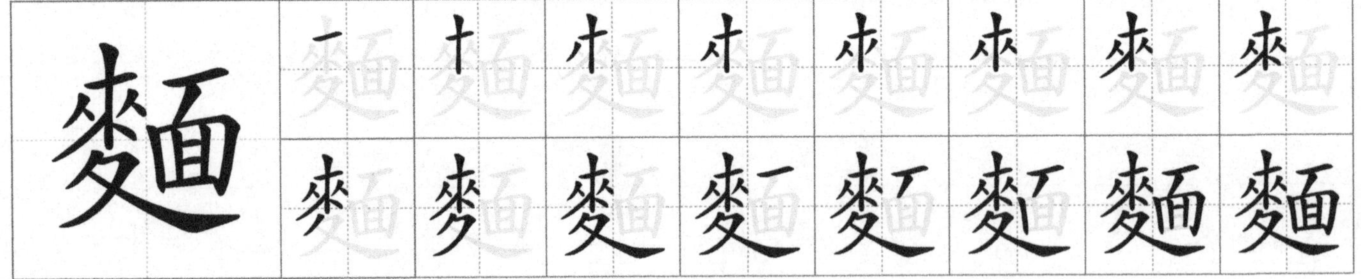

LEARN

UNICODE SIM.	UNICODE TRAD.
40629	38754

TRADITIONAL

面

WRITE

trace and draw this letter in the cells below

一 丆 丆 而 而 而 而 而 面

LEARN

面 面 面

PRACTICE

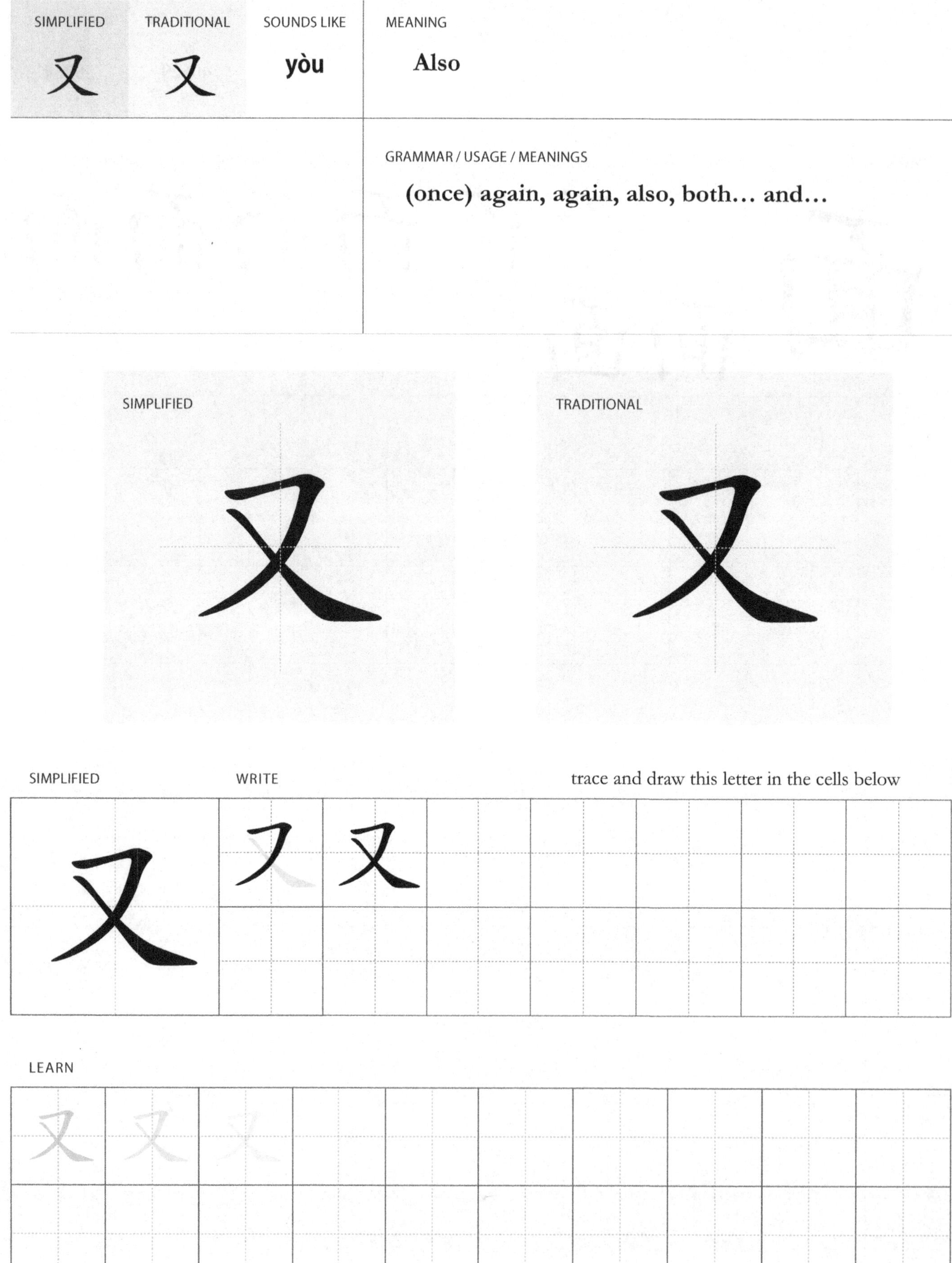
SIMPLIFIED
又
TRADITIONAL
又
SOUNDS LIKE
yòu
MEANING
Also
GRAMMAR / USAGE / MEANINGS
(once) again, again, also, both… and…
SIMPLIFIED
TRADITIONAL
SIMPLIFIED
WRITE
trace and draw this letter in the cells below
LEARN

UNICODE SIM.	UNICODE TRAD.
21448	21448

TRADITIONAL

又

WRITE

trace and draw this letter in the cells below

LEARN

PRACTICE

SIMPLIFIED	TRADITIONAL	SOUNDS LIKE	MEANING
定	定	dìng	Set

GRAMMAR / USAGE / MEANINGS

certainly, to set, to fix, surely, to determine, fixed, to decide, to order, to calm down, calm

SIMPLIFIED

定

TRADITIONAL

定

SIMPLIFIED WRITE trace and draw this letter in the cells below

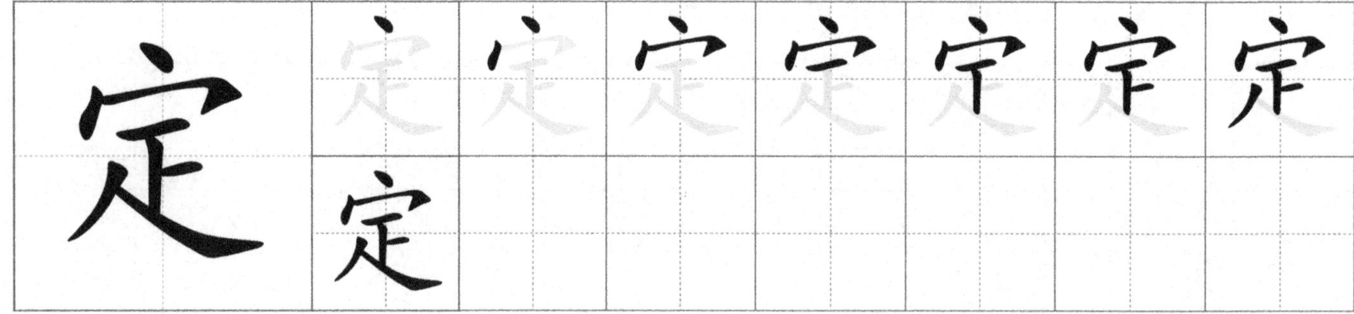

LEARN

UNICODE SIM.	UNICODE TRAD.
23450	23450

TRADITIONAL

定

WRITE

trace and draw this letter in the cells below

定

LEARN

PRACTICE

SIMPLIFIED	TRADITIONAL	SOUNDS LIKE	MEANING
见	見	jiàn / xiàn	See

GRAMMAR / USAGE / MEANINGS

to see, to meet, to appear (to be something), to interview / appear, view, opinion

SIMPLIFIED

见

TRADITIONAL

見

SIMPLIFIED WRITE trace and draw this letter in the cells below

LEARN

UNICODE SIM.	UNICODE TRAD.
35265	35211

TRADITIONAL

見

WRITE

trace and draw this letter in the cells below

丨 冂 月 月 目 貝 見

LEARN

見 見 見

PRACTICE

SIMPLIFIED	TRADITIONAL	SOUNDS LIKE	MEANING
只	隻	**zhī／zhǐ**	**Only**

GRAMMAR / USAGE / MEANINGS

lonely, measure word for one of a pair, only, just, but, single

TRADITIONAL

隻

SIMPLIFIED　　WRITE　　trace and draw this letter in the cells below

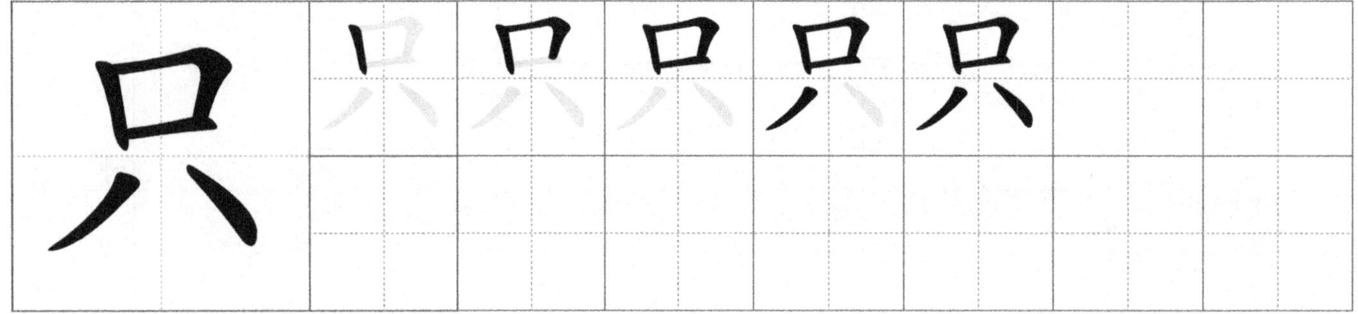

LEARN

只 只 只

UNICODE SIM.	UNICODE TRAD.
21482	38587

TRADITIONAL

WRITE

trace and draw this letter in the cells below

隻	丿	亻	亻	仁	仨	佳	隹
	隹	隻	隻				

LEARN

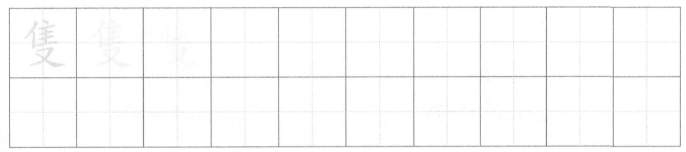

PRACTICE

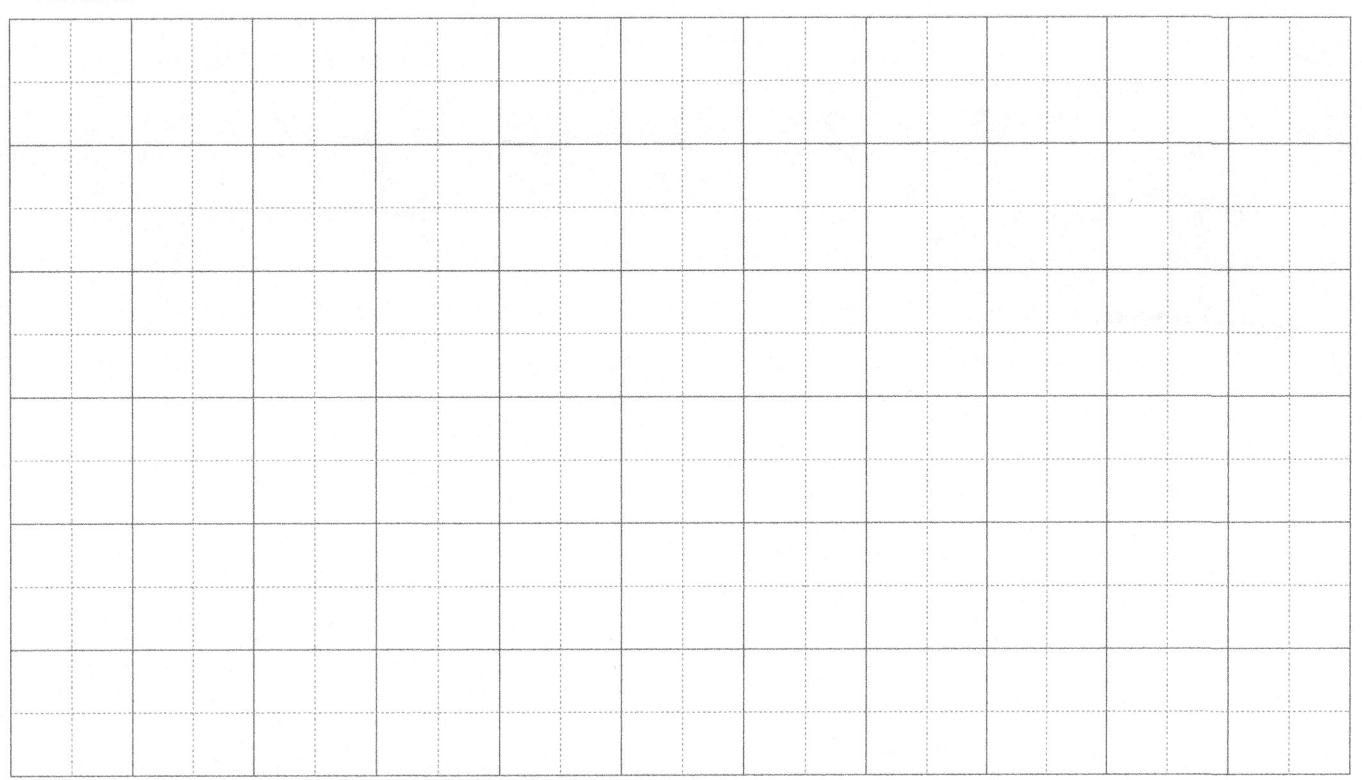

SIMPLIFIED	TRADITIONAL	SOUNDS LIKE	MEANING
主	主	**zhǔ**	**Main**

GRAMMAR / USAGE / MEANINGS

to own, main, subjective, to host, to advocate, lord, master, primary, host, God, opinion, to manage

SIMPLIFIED

主

TRADITIONAL

主

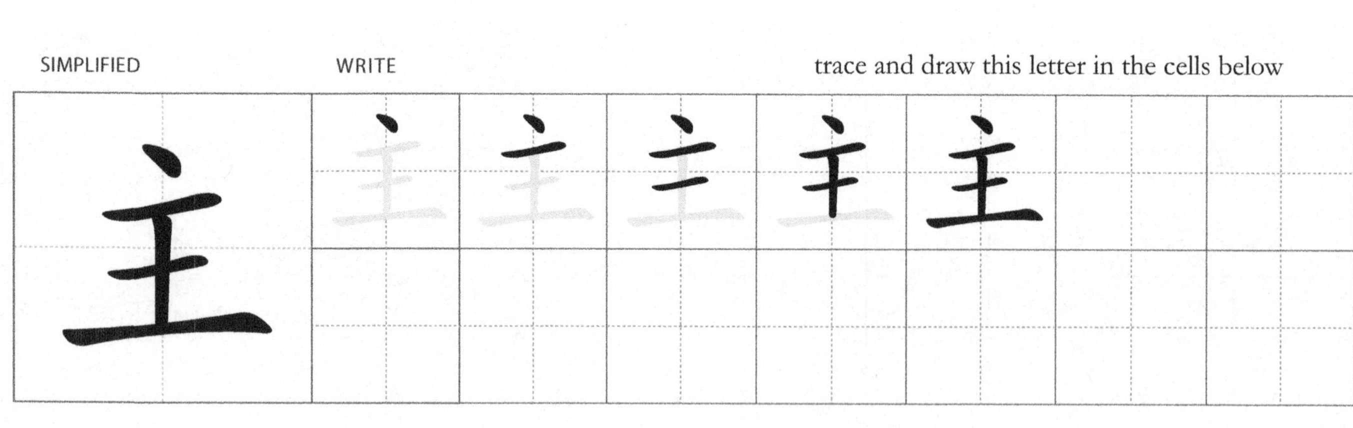

LEARN

UNICODE SIM.	UNICODE TRAD.
20027	20027

TRADITIONAL

主

WRITE

trace and draw this letter in the cells below

LEARN

PRACTICE

SIMPLIFIED	TRADITIONAL	SOUNDS LIKE	MEANING
没	沒	méi／mò	No

GRAMMAR / USAGE / MEANINGS

have not, be without, be inferior to, less than, not / sink, overflow, disappear, die (negative prefix for verbs)

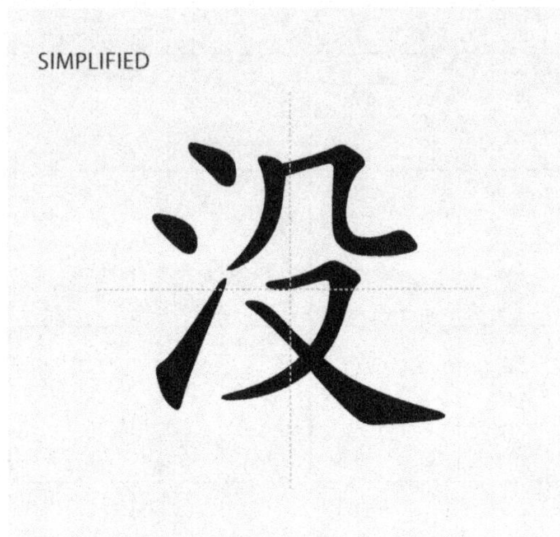

TRADITIONAL

沒

SIMPLIFIED WRITE trace and draw this letter in the cells below

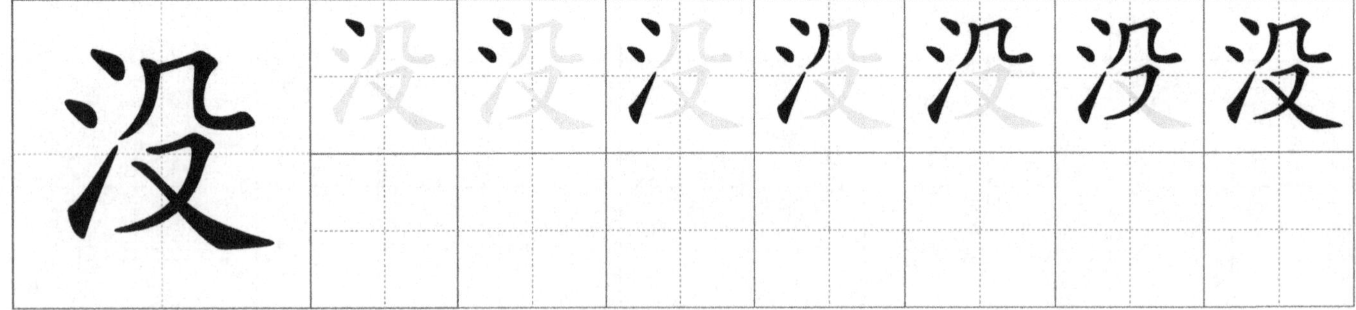

LEARN

UNICODE SIM.	UNICODE TRAD.
27809	**27794**

TRADITIONAL

没

WRITE

trace and draw this letter in the cells below

LEARN

PRACTICE

SIMPLIFIED	TRADITIONAL	SOUNDS LIKE	MEANING
公	公	gōng	Public

GRAMMAR / USAGE / MEANINGS

fair and just, public affairs, public, honorable (designation), authority, common, international, male, publicize

SIMPLIFIED

公

TRADITIONAL

公

SIMPLIFIED　　WRITE　　trace and draw this letter in the cells below

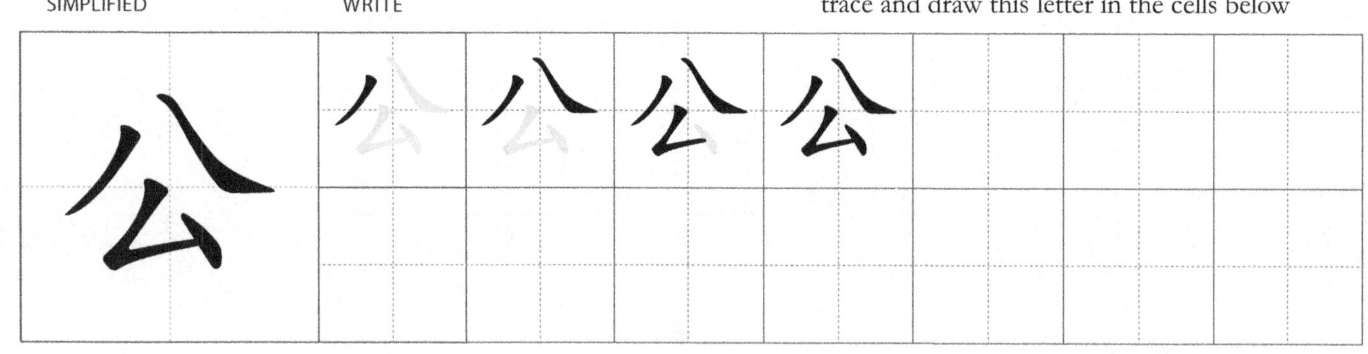

LEARN

公 公 公

UNICODE SIM.	UNICODE TRAD.
20844	20844

TRADITIONAL

公

WRITE

trace and draw this letter in the cells below

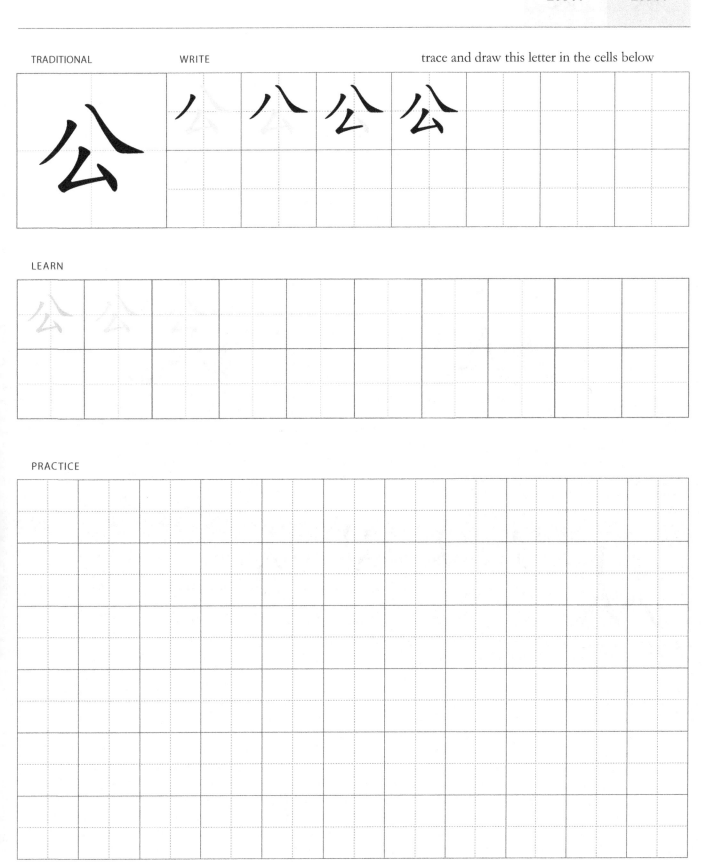

丿 八 公 公

LEARN

公 公 公

PRACTICE

SIMPLIFIED	TRADITIONAL	SOUNDS LIKE	MEANING
从	從	**cóng**	From

GRAMMAR / USAGE / MEANINGS

from, follower, since, join, obey, follow, observe

SIMPLIFIED

从

TRADITIONAL

從

SIMPLIFIED

从

WRITE

trace and draw this letter in the cells below

LEARN

UNICODE SIM.	UNICODE TRAD.
20174	24478

TRADITIONAL

從

WRITE

trace and draw this letter in the cells below

LEARN

PRACTICE

Part 3

PINYIN
TIAN ZI GE

Part 4

FLASH CARDS

PHOTOCOPY OR
CUT OUT & KEEP

S 的 T 的
S 一 T 一
S 是 T 是
S 不 T 不
S 了 T 了
S 人 T 人
S 我 T 我
S 在 T 在
S 有 T 有

SOUNDS LIKE
shì
MEANING
Yes

SOUNDS LIKE
yī
MEANING
One

SOUNDS LIKE
de
MEANING
Of

SOUNDS LIKE
rén
MEANING
People

SOUNDS LIKE
le/liăo
MEANING
Up

SOUNDS LIKE
bù
MEANING
No

SOUNDS LIKE
yǒu
MEANING
There Are

SOUNDS LIKE
zài
MEANING
In

SOUNDS LIKE
wǒ
MEANING
I

S 他 T 他
S 这 T 這
S 为 T 為
S 之 T 之
S 大 T 大
S 来 T 来
S 以 T 以
S 个 T 個
S 中 T 中

SOUNDS LIKE
wéi / wèi
MEANING
For

SOUNDS LIKE
zhè
MEANING
This

SOUNDS LIKE
tā
MEANING
He

SOUNDS LIKE
lái
MEANING
Come

SOUNDS LIKE
dà
MEANING
Big

SOUNDS LIKE
zhī
MEANING
Of

SOUNDS LIKE
zhōng
MEANING
Middle

SOUNDS LIKE
gè
MEANING
Individual

SOUNDS LIKE
yǐ
MEANING
With

S 上 T 上
S 们 T 們
S 到 T 到
S 说 T 説
S 国 T 國
S 和 T 和
S 地 T 地
S 也 T 也
S 子 T 子

SOUNDS LIKE
dào
MEANING
To

SOUNDS LIKE
men
MEANING
We

SOUNDS LIKE
shàng
MEANING
On

SOUNDS LIKE
hé / huò
MEANING
And

SOUNDS LIKE
guó
MEANING
Country

SOUNDS LIKE
shuō
MEANING
Says

SOUNDS LIKE
zǐ
MEANING
Son

SOUNDS LIKE
yě
MEANING
Also

SOUNDS LIKE
de / dì
MEANING
Ground

S 时 T 時
S 道 T 道
S 出 T 出
S 而 T 而
S 要 T 要
于 於 OR 于
S 就 T 就
S 下 T 下
S 得 T 得

SOUNDS LIKE
chū
MEANING
Out

SOUNDS LIKE
dào
MEANING
Road

SOUNDS LIKE
shí
MEANING
Time

SOUNDS LIKE
yú
MEANING
At

SOUNDS LIKE
yào / yāo
MEANING
Want

SOUNDS LIKE
ér
MEANING
And

SOUNDS LIKE
dé / de / děi
MEANING
Have To

SOUNDS LIKE
xià
MEANING
Down

SOUNDS LIKE
jiù
MEANING
Just

S	T	S	T	S	T
可	可	你	你	年	年
生	生	自	自	会	會
那	那	后	後	能	能

SOUNDS LIKE
nián
MEANING
Year

SOUNDS LIKE
nǐ
MEANING
You

SOUNDS LIKE
kě
MEANING
Can

SOUNDS LIKE
huì
MEANING
Meeting

SOUNDS LIKE
zì
MEANING
Since

SOUNDS LIKE
shēng
MEANING
Born

SOUNDS LIKE
néng
MEANING
Can

SOUNDS LIKE
hòu
MEANING
After

SOUNDS LIKE
nà
MEANING
That

S	T		S	T		S	T
对	對		着	著		事	事
其	其		里	裏 OR 裡		所	所
去	去		行	行		过	過

SOUNDS LIKE
shì
MEANING
Thing

SOUNDS LIKE
zhe/zhuó/zhāo/zháo
MEANING
Write

SOUNDS LIKE
duì
MEANING
Right

SOUNDS LIKE
suǒ
MEANING
Place

SOUNDS LIKE
lǐ
MEANING
Inside

SOUNDS LIKE
qí
MEANING
Its

SOUNDS LIKE
guò
MEANING
Over

SOUNDS LIKE
háng / xíng
MEANING
Line

SOUNDS LIKE
qù
MEANING
Go

S	T	S	T	S	T
家	家	十	十	用	用
发	發 OR 髮	天	天	如	如
然	然	作	作	方	方

SOUNDS LIKE

yòng

MEANING

Use

SOUNDS LIKE

shí

MEANING

Ten

SOUNDS LIKE

jiā

MEANING

Home

SOUNDS LIKE

rú

MEANING

As

SOUNDS LIKE

tiān

MEANING

Sky

SOUNDS LIKE

fā / fà

MEANING

Simplified = Hair,
Traditional 發 = to send ;
髮 = Hair

SOUNDS LIKE

fāng

MEANING

Square

SOUNDS LIKE

zuò

MEANING

Do

SOUNDS LIKE

rán

MEANING

Yet

S T
成 成
S T
者 者
S T
多 多
S T
日 日
S T
都 都
S T
三 三
S T
小 小
S T
军 軍
S T
二 二

SOUNDS LIKE
duō
MEANING
More

SOUNDS LIKE
zhě
MEANING
The

SOUNDS LIKE
chéng
MEANING
Become

SOUNDS LIKE
sān
MEANING
Three

SOUNDS LIKE
dōu
MEANING
Both

SOUNDS LIKE
rì
MEANING
Day

SOUNDS LIKE
èr
MEANING
Two

SOUNDS LIKE
jūn
MEANING
Military

SOUNDS LIKE
xiǎo
MEANING
Small

S T
无 無
S T
同 同
S T
么 麼
S T
经 經
S T
法 法
S T
当 當
S T
起 起
S T
与 與
S T
好 好

SOUNDS LIKE

me

MEANING

What?

SOUNDS LIKE

tóng

MEANING

Same

SOUNDS LIKE

wú

MEANING

None

SOUNDS LIKE

dāng / dàng

MEANING

When

SOUNDS LIKE

fǎ

MEANING

Law

SOUNDS LIKE

jīng

MEANING

Through

SOUNDS LIKE

hǎo / hào

MEANING

Good

SOUNDS LIKE

yú / yǔ / yù

MEANING

With

SOUNDS LIKE

qǐ

MEANING

Start

S 看 T 看
S 学 T 學
S 进 T 進
S 种 T 種
S 将 T 將
S 还 T 還
S 分 T 分
S 此 T 此
S 心 T 心

SOUNDS LIKE

jìn

MEANING

Enter

SOUNDS LIKE

xué

MEANING

Learning

SOUNDS LIKE

kān / kàn

MEANING

Watch

SOUNDS LIKE

hái / huán

MEANING

Also

SOUNDS LIKE

jiāng / jiàng

MEANING

Will

SOUNDS LIKE

zhǒng / zhòng

MEANING

Species

SOUNDS LIKE

xīn

MEANING

Heart

SOUNDS LIKE

cǐ

MEANING

This

SOUNDS LIKE

fēn / fèn

MEANING

Points

S
T
前
前
S
T
麵
面
S
T
又
又
S
T
定
定
S
T
见
見
S
T
只
隻
S
T
主
主
S
T
没
没
S
T
公
公

SOUNDS LIKE
yòu
MEANING
Also

SOUNDS LIKE
miàn
MEANING
Noodles

SOUNDS LIKE
qián
MEANING
Front

SOUNDS LIKE
zhī / zhǐ
MEANING
Only

SOUNDS LIKE
jiàn / xiàn
MEANING
See

SOUNDS LIKE
dìng
MEANING
Set

SOUNDS LIKE
gōng
MEANING
Public

SOUNDS LIKE
méi / mò
MEANING
No

SOUNDS LIKE
zhǔ
MEANING
Main

S 从 T 從	S T	S T
S T	S T	S T
S T	S T	S T

SOUNDS LIKE MEANING	SOUNDS LIKE MEANING	SOUNDS LIKE **cóng** MEANING **From**
SOUNDS LIKE MEANING	SOUNDS LIKE MEANING	SOUNDS LIKE MEANING
SOUNDS LIKE MEANING	SOUNDS LIKE MEANING	SOUNDS LIKE MEANING

謝謝

Xièxiè

Thank you!

Thank you for choosing our book!

You are now well on your way to learning how to read, write and speak Chinese, and we hope that you enjoyed our Simplified and Traditional workbook.

If you enjoyed learning with us, we would very much like to hear about your progress in a review!

We are always eager to learn if there is anything we can do to make our books better for future students. We are committed to making the best language learning content available so please do get in touch with us via email if you had a problem with any of the content in this book:

hello@polyscholar.com

POLYSCHOLAR

www.polyscholar.com

Made in the USA
Las Vegas, NV
26 December 2023